# ALZHEIMER'S DISEASE

# ALZHEIMER'S
## DISEASE

Courage
for Those
Who Care

Martha O. Adams

United Church Press
Cleveland, Ohio

United Church Press, Cleveland, Ohio 44115
© 1999 by Martha O. Adams

Original edition published by Abbey Press as *Alzheimer's Disease: A Call to Courage for Caregivers*,
© 1986 by Martha O. Adams.

NOTE: This book is not intended to replace legal, financial, or medical counsel. Always consult your attorney, financial planner, or doctor about legal, financial, and medical matters.

Library of Congress Cataloging-in-Publication Data
Adams, Martha O.
    Alzheimer's disease : courage for those who care / by Martha O. Adams.
      p.   cm.
    Includes bibliographical references.
    ISBN 0-8298-1304-7 (pbk. : alk. paper)
    1. Alzheimer's disease—Patients—Care.   I. Title.
    RC523.A325   1999
    362.1'6831—dc21                                                          98-48409
                                                                                      CIP

To my mother and father:

"No one has greater love than this,
to lay down one's life for one's friends."

—John 15:13

# Contents

# Author's Note

To write this book was an act of faith. To read it is an act of courage. We are threatened by the same fear that grips the physician who cannot confront patients with a full and honest diagnosis of any dread disease. It is the fear that if they are told, they may give up hope.

If you suspect you have Alzheimer's disease (AD) or if a loved one has received the probable diagnosis, pause to consider your reasons for knowing more. If fear is your motivation, you will find much within these pages to feed that fear. If hope is a stranger to you, you will find ample material here to reinforce your habit of hopelessness. Such indulgence will do more harm than good.

If, however, you come to this reading out of a need to meet the future better equipped; to learn to refocus on what is good; to listen with tender ear to the hard-won wisdom of those who have gone before you; to hone the tools that will serve you best—patience, persistence, love, and willingness to look to others for help with tough decisions—then this book is written for you. You walk with heroes.

This book combines personal study and experimentation in living and caregiving. Members of my Alzheimer's support groups, friends, acquaintances, and strangers, generously reaching out to help and be helped, have encouraged me and inspired my writing through poignant stories and hard learnings they have shared. In these pages they speak in steadfast advocacy born of experience. I thank them all.

I am indebted to my father for his willingness to expose the trials he has faced, but more for the courage and grace with which he has endured. I am grateful for the help in the first edition of Rachel Billington and the Education Committee of the Alzheimer's Disease and Related Disorders Association, now known as the Alzheimer's Association, and for many voices of expertise in the fields of medicine, law, and nursing care.

I extend a sharp salute to Adrienne Wolfert, author and teacher, for suggesting I tackle this project and for her encouragement in the writing of this book. For her consistent high standard of writing, and for my writing comrades who challenge and nurture one another in the solitary task of writing, I am most grateful.

Susan Winslow's unlimited interest in whatever is roiling in my head and heart and her faithful friendship will be remembered. I thank United Church Press for taking on the publishing of this revised edition, which looked so simple at the outset. The cheerful encouragement of my editor, Kim Sadler, and Kelley Baker's speedy responses to my questions helped make the work a continuing labor of love. The patient, steadfast support of my husband, Bob, endured throughout the simultaneous work of our relocation to North Carolina and the revision of the first edition.

# FOREWORD

Elias E. Manuelidis studied medicine at the University of Munich, Germany, and graduated in 1942. He studied pathology from 1943 to 1946 at the Institute of Pathology in Munich and subsequently was appointed director of the Pathological Anatomical Laboratory of the German Research Institute of Psychiatry, Max Planck Institute, in Munich for three years. In 1949 he directed the laboratories of the Hospital of the International Refugees Organization in Munich for a year and spent a year as a civilian neuropathologist of the Ninety-eighth General Hospital, United States Army, European Command.

He joined the faculty of Yale University School of Medicine in 1951 and was professor of neuropathology and neurology at the time of the first edition of this book in 1986. He was a visiting scientist at the National Institute of Neurological Diseases and Blindness, National Institutes of Health; visiting lecturer of neuroanatomy, Harvard University; past president of the American Association of Neuropathologists; and has served on advisory committees of the National Institutes of Health and Multiple Sclerosis Society. In 1985, Gov. William O'Neill of Connecticut appointed Dr. Manuelidis as a member of the task force to study the needs and problems of persons suffering from Alzheimer's disease. He worked on dementias from 1975 until the time of his death in 1996. The National Institutes of Health and the Commonwealth Fund supported his research.

Though much has changed in the knowledge base and policy field related to Alzheimer's disease, Dr. Manuelidis's foreword to the first edition of this book remains timely today.

———•◦•◦•———

Dr. Lewis Thomas, a prominent biomedical scientist, called dementias "the disease of the century." Dementias are the third or fourth most common group of diseases affecting individuals sixty-five years of age or older. Alzheimer's disease accounts for more than 50 percent of the cases of dementia. According to some statistics, as many as four million Americans sixty-five or older suffer from Alzheimer's disease. This group of individuals constitutes the largest-growing segment of our population. Thus, it is projected that there will be a rapid rise of Alzheimer's disease.[1] Accordingly, federal funds for long-term care will increase from the present level of $12 billion a year (in 1986) to $43 billion a year by the end of the century. The care of patients with Alzheimer's disease will account for up to 50 percent of this expenditure.

Alzheimer's disease is first detected clinically by loss of memory for recent events and mild intellectual deterioration. With the passing of time, the cognitive impairment progresses and is associated with personality changes, irritability, depression, and severe disorientation about time and space. Ultimately, patients lose all their intellectual abilities and reach a stage of complete vegetation, unable to recognize even close family members. Victims do not die from Alzheimer's disease but from other intercurrent diseases, such as pneumonia, bedsores, and sepsis. Therefore, death certificates do not accurately reflect the true incidence of Alzheimer's disease. The progression and duration of the illness vary considerably. The course of the disease is more rapid in younger patients than in older individuals, and in some of the latter cases the disease may last for years or even decades.

In many instances the clinical diagnosis of Alzheimer's disease may be very difficult. Accordingly, a second expert opinion in such instances is absolutely justified. Other diseases that can be confused with Alzheimer's disease are multi-infarct dementia (caused by multiple strokes), general forms of cerebral vascular disease, normal pressure hydrocephalus, nutritional deficiencies, amyotrophic lateral sclerosis, Parkinson's disease, and dementias accompanying tumors and brain injuries. Whereas Alzheimer's disease constitutes about 50 percent of dementia cases in the elderly, multi-infarct dementia accounts for only 17 percent, and 18 percent are of mixed etiology. Some of the apparent dementias, such as depression, are treatable and curable. However, it is of utmost importance to eliminate clinically several conditions causing dementia from the group of Alzheimer's disease. Unfortunately, at the present time there are no laboratory procedures or X-ray examinations that are unequivocally diagnostic of Alzheimer's disease.

Dr. Alois Alzheimer was the first to describe the diagnostic brain changes seen postmortem in individuals suffering from Alzheimer's disease. Two types of lesions are characteristic of Alzheimer's disease: (1) senile or neuritic plaques represent extracellular deposits of protein and other cellular debris in the brain; and (2) neurofibrillary tangles or fiberlike proteins accumulate inside the nerve cells. The clinical findings and these structural changes observed in the brain make Alzheimer's disease a specific and characteristic disease entity. It should be emphasized that Alzheimer's disease has nothing to do with the natural and inevitable course of aging. Furthermore, Alzheimer's disease is not the result of the hardening of the arteries of the brain. On the contrary, arteriosclerosis is not a characteristic feature of Alzheimer's disease.

The causes of Alzheimer's disease are unknown at the present time. Scientists in the United States and throughout the world have developed several hypotheses to explain the etiology of this disease. Some of the findings may be a result rather than a cause of the disease. For example, some investigators have been impressed by the abnormal protein deposits in the brain, but it is likely that these represent end-stage degenerative changes rather than etiological products. Similarly, some investigators think that Alzheimer's disease is the result of the specified destruction of cholinergic nerve cells in the cerebrum, but the etiology of these changes is not clear. Others have postulated a toxic etiology, such as aluminum. Some investigators believe there is a disturbance in the blood flow to the cerebrum, and others postulate an infectious etiology for Alzheimer's disease. Finally, some observers are exploring the possible genetic basis of Alzheimer's disease, as there are some familial clusters of this entity.

Based upon these hypotheses and observations, researchers are pursuing their studies in several laboratories throughout the country. It is not the purpose of this introduction to evaluate critically the pros and cons of all the major hypotheses that careful workers advance in explaining the etiology of Alzheimer's disease. However, a few comments are appropriate concerning the genetic hypothesis. This notion is based upon the observation that in 10 to 15 percent of Alzheimer's cases there is familial incidence. Although 85 percent of the cases constitute isolated sporadic manifestations of this condition, no chromosomal abnormalities have yet been found in Alzheimer's disease. Indeed, a specific genetic background may constitute only an unusual predisposition in certain families to a still-unknown noxious etiological factor. For all practical purposes, no anxiety is justified or appropriate for most family members about their own predisposition to this dreadful disease.

Alzheimer's disease is debilitating for both the patients and their families. It is worse than cancer; a cancer victim recognizes his surroundings, can communicate with family and friends, and is cognizant of the tender care of both family and community up to the last stages of his or her life. An Alzheimer victim, however, is intellectually and emotionally mute. An impenetrable concrete wall descends between the afflicted person and the world. Relatives of these patients and some government authorities recognize the dreadful and tragic effects of Alzheimer's disease. They are now more committed to finding a cure for this debilitating condition.

However, relatives and the public should remember that doctors treat rather than cure disease. We effectively treat coronary disease by vascular bypasses without curing the underlying arterial illness. We treat diabetes by injecting patients with insulin without actually curing the underlying disease of the pancreas, and subsequently patients enjoy many fruitful and productive years. We can also rather effectively treat Parkinson's disease with drug injections, although we don't have knowledge of the exact causes of the disease. At the present time there is no prevention and no cure for patients with Alzheimer's disease. There are, however, palliative types of treatment—prevention of infection and accident, antidepressant drugs and psychotherapy—that can help the victims and family members cope with the manifestation of Alzheimer's disease.

I spent twenty-five years of my professional life as a laboratory worker in the ivory tower of Yale University. Five years ago I gave a talk to a community support group in southern Connecticut. A turning point occurred in my life when I participated in this community affair where both family members and victims were present. The magnitude of the intellectual, emotional, and financial problems that affect families became clear to me. Subsequently, I was instrumental in organizing a chapter of Alzheimer's Disease and Related Disorders Association (now the Alzheimer's Association) in southern Connecticut. I met several family members, and the pride and dignity with which they were facing their horrible fate touched me. In my own professional life, it was a rewarding experience to meet relatives who cooperated well with the doctors treating their sick relatives. Their cooperation extends not only to clinical treatment but encompasses research efforts and postmortem examinations. There is a decline of autopsy rates throughout the United States, but at Yale New Haven Hospital we have almost 100 percent permission to perform postmortem examinations on victims with Alzheimer's disease. Family members deserve attention, help, and cooperation from government agencies and the community. Friends of the family and members of the community—especially those who are retired and in good health—can do a great deal of good by helping the victims and their relatives on a voluntary basis.

This book by Martha Adams focuses on the interactions between the victims, family members, friends, and community. It emphasizes practical aspects of the many problems facing such families. She shares with her readers her personal experiences and feelings as a caregiver for one who has Alzheimer's disease. Further, she relates the experiences of others who have a similar task. Ms. Adams also outlines valuable answers and resources for solutions to functional problems that arise in families who have the responsibility of caring for someone afflicted with dementia. She dares to show her humanity, which I believe will provide encouragement and hope to those who find themselves dealing with loved ones who suffer from this tragic disease.

Elias E. Manuelidis, M.D.
April 4, 1986

## POSTSCRIPT

The introduction by my late husband is as meaningful now as in 1986, when it first was written. Alzheimer's disease continues to take its toll and challenges us all to have courage. I have little to add to the introduction above but would like you to know the motto my husband posted on the door of his office, the one that he proclaimed even when things seemed most bleak. Perhaps it will have some value for others.

*Dum spiro spero.*
(As long as I breathe, I hope.)

Laura Manuelidis, M.D.
Professor and Head of Neuropathology
Yale University School of Medicine
January 1998

## CONVERSATIONS WITH A PRIMARY CAREGIVER

WHEN I INVITED my father to write something to accompany this book, he expressed appreciation but also a feeling of inadequacy. He could offer little to caregivers, he said, that would add to whatever else had already been written. We sat together one evening after we put Mother to bed and talked quietly.

Just a month prior to that evening, Mother had suffered an "episode" the physician and a neurologist could not identify. She became comatose, unable to move about, incontinent, unable to speak. My brother was there and I spoke with him by phone that night. He felt Mother had only hours to live. Dad told me he was convinced he was faced with all the problems of Mother's being immobile and practically unable to communicate. However, the next morning she awoke and seemed normal, and they resumed their lives with gratitude. We talked about it.

"You can say what you want. For me it was as miraculous as having someone die and come back to life again. I am grateful beyond measure that she was not incapacitated to the point of needing immediate nursing home care, that we still have time left to be together.

"This whole thing is a humbling experience. I've found some of the thoughts from Ronald Wells's book and our daily devotions a great help in trying to look at the thing objectively.1 At no time have I, consciously at least, felt sorry for myself. Others have faced far worse things and have been able to endure them. Read the story of Job, a tremendous story of faith and an illustration of how to face extremely adverse ordeals. That inspires me."

"But, Dad!" I protested, "Job gives us permission to feel sorry for ourselves and complain about our lot, even though we remain faithful. He raged against God! That seems human."

He shook his head. "When a person starts feeling abused...," his voice trailed off. "Well, let's say my goal from day to day is just to try to find solutions to the problems. My primary concern all the way through has been to keep myself together so I can finish the job."

I questioned: "What can the church do to be helpful for you?" He responded: "Educate. Teach people how to relate to disabled persons. For the first time in our lives, I've learned about the 'apartness' of the disabled. My hearing problem separates us; it requires more effort on the part of others. People don't know how to respond to your mother; they tend to smile politely and keep their distance. Granted, she gets things confused, but people need to be reminded that she still has feelings, expectations, and needs for contact. I guess people don't want to offend and feel it's safer not to get involved. It's true, she can come out with the darndest statements at times and it throws people. But every Sunday there are some who make a point of greeting us warmly, putting an arm around your mother and just letting her know they're glad to see her. That alone is worth the effort to get there."

"When you were sick, Dad, and I took Mother to church, I noticed she can't follow the hymns anymore. But she still earnestly participates in the liturgy that she's known for years, the Lord's Prayer, and the doxology as though they serve as a vital connection for her."

"Yes, I'm convinced of it. 'Connections,' as you call them, though dim, maybe vague, are still there for her. There is little else we do which has such a history for her, for both of us." Then softly, "To be among worshiping people helps me, too."

His voice faltered. "Unquestionably there are people at the church who are willing to help, but no organization there really offers anything other than a sympathetic word. If someone would take Dorothy under her wing for a morning, perhaps to attend a women's meeting at the church, and I knew I could pick her up an hour or two later, that would be a grand thing."

We talked about coping with frustration. "At times I lose my patience. It provokes me when I do. It's a weakness on my part. It doesn't happen too often now, but even once is too often. It's a situation we're confronted with and we do the best we can with it. I'm always fighting time. I'm so darn far behind on things here that need doing.

"I deliberately try to kid with her. I find kidding tremendously helpful. After such a session I'll often say, 'We have a lot of fun together, don't we?' and she'll agree. Sometimes *she* even makes the remark. Every once in a while people will observe how sweet and pleasant she is. I can only say I wish they had known her ten or fifteen years ago. When I think of the way she used to buzz around and do things...that's the hardest part, seeing her marvelous vitality and personality wither away.

"I've thought many times about our decision to move to Florida. Tough as it was, I can't think of a better solution for us. I don't know where we could find people any nicer than they are here. Good food, and this pleasant climate lets us be outdoors in fresh air and sunshine. These are positive factors for us both. I'm grateful that the progression of this disease with your mother is as slow as it has been.

"Where does hope fit into this picture? Hoping for some restorative miracle to reactivate her destroyed faculties is beyond the realm of reason. The most we can hope for is our staying together and doing things the very best way we can one day at a time. In spite of the problems, there are many ways the situation could be much more difficult. I'm eternally grateful for what we've got."

We said a gentle good night. I sat in the evening silence thinking about gratitude and courage. Like a beacon in a dark night, Dad's courage reaches far beyond the boundaries of the family. It lights the way not only for all who know him now, but for those who will hear later of his courage and be changed.

As I put my notebook away, a slip of paper slid from the shelf onto the floor of the small living room. I recognized my own printing. The ink was faded, but the message I'd sent them by Elizabeth Gray Vining was still clear:

Consider thy old friends, O God, whose years are increasing. Provide for them homes of dignity and freedom. Give them, in case of need, understanding helpers and the willingness to accept help.

Deepen their joy in the beauty of thy world and their love for their neighbors. Grant them courage in the face of pain or weakness, and always a sure knowledge of thy presence.[2]
Amen.

Martha O. Adams
March 19, 1985

It is a brightly washed sunny day here in Key Largo in February 1998, and I am writing and visiting with my father. Preparing for the updated revision of this book, I came across some letters of his.

From his letter of August 28, 1986: "I understand all you are saying concerning our situation. The finality of the last parting I'm sure is nearly always difficult, and I know it will be for me. There are still times she is definitely aware of what's going on. I believe the only sentence she spoke today was as I was opening the screen door. She said, 'Can I go with you?' I was surprised and pleased. I know very well she would feel abandoned if put in a nursing home now. The time will come when there will not be that awareness and then a change can be made. I feel this is part of my job before I hang up my spurs, so we'll carry on as best we can for the present. The tangible help, support, and love you and the rest of our wonderful family give mean a great deal to me. Likewise, local concern, love, and the desire to be helpful by so many are a real support."

Later that year, Dad was told that he needed cataract surgery, and because he was having to do so much lifting of Mother, he must find arrangements for her care. After several months of careful searching, he found a nursing home especially for those with dementia. Constructed in a quadrangle, with each room opening onto a garden surrounded by a wide boardwalk, this 1950s refurbished one-story motel would be a place of freedom for Mother to roam without threat. Before making the decision, Dad visited there on several occasions.

Meeting with the director, Dad and I asked many questions and were satisfied that this would be a good place for Mother. We had already had the discussion about brain autopsy upon death, and contact had been made with the Alzheimer's research group at the University of Miami

Medical Center. We informed the director of the nursing home of this and instructions were entered immediately into Mother's record, along with the name of the local funeral director we'd contacted, who would need to be the link between nursing home and medical center.

About four months after that excruciatingly painful day when we left her at the nursing home, and Dad was healing from his eye surgery, my sisters and I convinced him to come north for a vacation. He'd been driving forty-five minutes to see Mother several times a week. His visit with us was a wonderfully relaxing change for him.

One late summer day we were sitting together, looking out over the lake behind our home and taking great delight in the blue-winged dragonflies darting about. There was a rich silence between us. I suddenly "saw" Mother's face out over the water about ten feet from us. She was smiling with such a radiant expression of joy and recognition—the memory of it still brings me to tears. I turned to Dad and suggested we call the nursing home to check on Mother. "That's a wonderful idea." We learned she was not doing well and the doctor was to see her within the hour. That night we received a call that she might not make it through the night, and before we could make the necessary travel plans, Mother completed her journey to a better place. (See "Establishing the Line," pp.126–27 in the "Poems" section.)

At the age of eighty-two, Dad met Rosemary, whose husband had died from Parkinson's disease, and brought her north to meet the family. They were sitting together like love-struck teenagers at our kitchen table, examining the papaya I had bought for them to see if it was "ready." I was at the kitchen sink, listening. Rosie said, "You know, Charles, I've heard papaya is so good for you it will cure almost anything!" "Oh, there's one thing I know it won't cure," he said emphatically. "Really? What's that?" "Loneliness."

That little insight into the profound loneliness Dad suffered for so long helped me bring Rosie into the circle of our family. The sense of true blessing has only deepened during their eight remarkably happy and active years of travel, snorkeling, cycling, gardening, and friendships. Though Dad has suffered severe setbacks with pneumonia and some falls in his ninetieth and ninety-first years, and he is much more frail now, his spirit of courage continues, as does the lasting bond of their love.

PART 1

# THE CHALLENGE

*There is a comfort in the strength of love;*
*'Twill make a thing endurable, which else*
*Would . . . break the heart.*

— WILLIAM WORDSWORTH, "MICHAEL"

# 1     BEGINNINGS

I SEE THEM NOW. They walk hand in hand. One walks with a sense of getting there, glancing perhaps at a shopping list. The other, face blank, stares in store windows or gazes about as though seeing these sights for the first time. I find myself wanting to stop and with a kindly gesture ask the caregiver, "How is it going for you?" Yet I don't have the courage to do that. My concern is caught in the same trap of silence that snares others, even old friends, keeping them from asking the question. Have they always been with us, these pilgrims of the aging? Or am I noticing them now because I am among these pilgrims?

The words "Alzheimer's disease" (AD) have become familiar to most people now, thanks to the work and care of many, but particularly the families of famous people such as Ronald Reagan who have been stricken. Victims of brain tumors, strokes, Parkinson's disease, multiple sclerosis, and a variety of other assaults to the brain share in the helpless, hopeless aura that surrounds the entire afflicted family. The fear associated with even the thought of Alzheimer's disease causes people of all mentalities to begin observing themselves and their patterns of forgetfulness with a scrutiny that can cause panic.

AD has been written about in books, newspapers, and magazines. One TV special after another has portrayed it. We've become familiar with the litany of ages and stages of the disease, the theories suggesting cause, and the research being done to discover breakthroughs in treatment and prevention. Why, then, another book on the subject?

Spirits were at a low ebb at a meeting of the local Alzheimer's support group. Members talked about creating a focus group to meet and discuss the idea of writing an exhaustive report on Alzheimer's disease. The opinions were uniform: "We don't need another book on AD. We have nothing new to say."

I looked around at these dispirited, gloomy, depressed people, and it occurred to me that I was in the company of heroes. They needed to be lifted, their voices and struggles and minor victories needed to be heard. Where are the words of practical advice for them? How do they learn to cope with this tragedy? What means of relief are available? What impact does this have on their religious faith? Are there words of hope?

My experience points to a variety of responses on the part of families and particularly the primary caregiver. The most disturbing response is a severe, unshakable depression that overwhelms some caregivers. The result is a double tragedy, with both the caregiver and the afflicted becoming dependent.

Peter Strauss, a New York City attorney whose practice has accommodated some two thousand AD clients in recent years, states: "In about half of our cases the 'well' caregiver is depressed or sliding into alcoholism. These people cannot deal with decisions they must make because they are so depressed."

For the most part, experience has put me in touch with courage in the face of pain, and humor in the midst of suffering. It has shown me, in acts of caring and love, the energy and self-discipline people summon from deep reserves day and night.

Our family's awareness of AD began in 1975, one year after Dad's retirement. Mother and Dad were visiting us en route to their great adventure: a three-month camping trip in Alaska. Dad had arranged all the particulars, and Mother seemed uninterested in discussing the trip or looking at maps with us. She brushed off any specific questions with a soon-familiar answer: "You'll have to ask your father about that." It was a puzzle but not a problem.

On their return trip they stayed with us long enough for me to notice disturbing lapses in Mother's memory. One bright afternoon she and I were in the kitchen preparing vegetables and laughing over stories about my daughter's recent dating experiences. Moments later Mother asked, "Has Laura been dating lately?" I was shocked. Mother knew immediately something was wrong. She quickly changed the subject and continued scraping carrots.

Before they left, I walked out to the garden with Dad and asked him if he had noticed such peculiar lapses. He confessed that he had, but he was convinced it was simply a matter of her not paying attention. I urged him to go to their doctor, discuss the situation with him, and have Mother undergo a complete physical examination. Reluctantly he agreed.

Several weeks later I received a letter: "I took your mother to the doctor and explained your concern. [Notice *his* concern remained hidden.] After he examined her, he told me my daughter should find something else to worry about. Your mother is in perfect health. As far as memory lapses go, we all find it more difficult to remember things as we get older. He said even he was forgetful at times." It took a long time to convince Dad that another opinion was in order.

We know now that difficulty in remembering and the skill to conceal forgetfulness mark the earliest stages of AD. Astonishment at such incidents of immediate memory loss is common. "I just told you that!" This angry retort, born out of frustration, often accompanies accusations of not concentrating. Such a response frightens the person into worrying that anything spoken will expose her or his forgetfulness. Communication begins to diminish. Usually in these early stages, the afflicted one is acutely aware of being confused. Neither partner wants to talk about the problem with the other or with anyone else.

## HELPFUL FAMILY RESPONSE

What is the helpful family response at this point? First and foremost, find a doctor who will deal with the problem seriously and maintain involvement. This is often easier said than done. As public awareness of this disease increases, some doctors are too quick to diagnose AD without the necessary complex testing.

A thorough physical is the first step. Make a record of all medications, vitamins, and food supplements being used by the patient and take it with you. List troublesome behavior, such as memory loss, confusion, overdependency, poor hygiene or table manners, withdrawal, or depression. As we have seen, there are numbers of treatable physical conditions that can cause similar symptoms.

Until there is an absolute diagnostic test for AD, analysis involves a thorough testing process. Diagnosis must be made by excluding many other diseases (see the Foreword). According to Dr. Andrea Schaffner, who was instrumental in developing the Yale New Haven Hospital Geriatric Assessment Clinic, each evaluation needs to be tailored to the individual patient. It is reasonable to expect your physician to include the following in an evaluation for suspected Alzheimer's disease:

- history of patient from both the patient and relative or friend
- mental-status examination
- complete physical
- neurological exam (not necessarily by a neurologist)
- CT (computerized tomography) scan, which takes X-ray images of the brain, or MRI (magnetic resonance imaging), and EEG (electroencephalogram), which detects abnormal brain wave activity. A physician may wish to use other tests, such as PET (positron emission tomography), which shows how different areas of the brain respond when one is engaged in various activities such as reading, or SPECT (single proton emission computed tomography), which shows how blood is circulating to the brain.
- blood tests for thyroid functions, serum B12, folic acid deficiencies, neurosyphillis, complete blood count, and numerous other metabolic functions.
- chest X ray, EKG

These tools are used to rule out other disease that could be causing symptoms.

It might be useful to add here that although arteriosclerosis is a separate disease process from AD and is not causally related to it, it remains quite possible for a person to suffer the simultaneous consequences of both diseases.

"Even after published studies clearly stated that most dementing illnesses in older people were due to something like Alzheimer's disease, people were still coming to my door telling me that they had been diagnosed as having 'hardening of the arteries,' " said Dr. Marsha Fretwell, assistant professor of medicine and chief of geriatric medicine at Roger Williams General Hospital in Providence, Rhode Island.

"It's interesting that that term has now been replaced by Alzheimer's. I'm not sure that's helpful. A lot of people are being labeled and told that nothing can be done. There are two risks here. Even if it's the right diagnosis, there are many things that can be done in managing drugs to improve function of the patient. If it's not the right diagnosis, you're missing possibilities for treatment. Patients and their families often ask, 'Why do you want to do a CT scan?' I explain that most people will show up normal. This allows us to diagnose the patient as having AD. The CT scan costs between $150 and $350 [in 1998 the cost was approximately $1,000]. My feeling is that if I'm going to label patients as demented, I've really changed their whole life. I've changed the way the reimbursement system will accept them. I've changed the way their doctors are going to treat them. I've changed the way their families will look at them. So before I do that to somebody, I'm going to be damned sure I haven't missed anything. If we don't want to pay for that, then that's society's problem. I don't have any problem doing a thorough evaluation to make sure the patient doesn't have a treatable problem."[1]

If your own physician is not willing to consider the symptoms seriously and thoroughly, begin asking questions about doctors who specialize in geriatric medicine. A call to hospitals, public health departments, or departments on aging is a good place to start. Attending a local Alzheimer support group is the richest source of information. Once you begin to communicate your concern, you will find others who have had to locate medical care for such problems. They will have opinions to share about the quality of their medical care.

Physicians are human, too, and can be somewhat overwhelmed by what a patient and family face with the enormous diagnosis of Alzheimer's disease. The inability to heal or cure is discouraging for physicians, and it can cause some to become emotionally paralyzed. For too many patients the diagnosis is given with little advice on how to cope. One of the members of the AD support group I attended told me his doctor examined his wife, told him she probably had AD, and said there was nothing he could do. "Call me if she gets violent" was the extent of his prescription and involvement.

Physicians could render great service by providing the nearest Alzheimer's Association contact number; having suggested reading lists and printed materials such as the Alzheimer's Association's Action Series pamphlets ("Steps to Getting a Diagnosis: Finding Out If It's Alzheimer's Disease"); identifying place and time of local AD support group meetings; giving information on other community services and resources for patients and families; and declaring in a straightforward way, "This is going to be tough and you're going to need lots of help along the way. I'll do all I can." This would set up a partnership approach.

If someone you care about needs to get this investigation and diagnosis under way but just can't quite face going through it, offer to make the appointment for them; take them and stay with them through the testing process. Be sure they have their glasses, hearing aids, medication records, insurance and social security information, and medical records.

Once a careful medical diagnosis is made, the next most important step is *to begin informing yourself about the legal responsibilities you now face.* If your parent or spouse has just been diagnosed with AD, you may still be in a numb state of disbelief and denial, oblivious to the ominous legal decisions that await you. If so, go to your calendar and make a notation to read chapter 2. Don't put it off too long. Brutal as it may sound, the family should seek legal counsel before the afflicted one becomes incompetent.

Become aware of the frequency of unusual lapses of memory or good judgment, and make notes for future appointments with your physician. Learn to empathize: "You're really having some trouble remembering. Is it becoming a problem for you? Let's work together and see if we can come up with some ways to help with the forgetfulness." For occasions of repeated questions or conversation, establish a simple signal, such as the subtle raising of a finger or slight shake of the head. Give this cue with affection, not criticism, out of a sense of helpfulness for each other, not embarrassment. A demonstration of cooperation can initiate a partnership approach to the problem of repeated conversations. This may help for a while.

None of us knew enough to communicate openly in this way. Mother's forgetfulness was a forbidden subject. It took three years of increasing loss and behind-the-scenes worrying before a CT scan and other neurological testing were done. The diagnosis showed that Mother had "presenile dementia of the Alzheimer's type which will probably proceed in a very slow fashion." That diagnosis proved to be exactly on target. Meanwhile, I began to read everything I could find on the subject.

In 1978 there wasn't very much to read. Considerably more is available today, although the research dollars needed to address the dramatic rise of HIV/AIDS has undoubtedly slowed the search for AD's cause and cure. Baby boomers are now turning fifty, and unless preventions are found fourteen million people could have AD by 2010, according to the Alzheimer's Association spring 1998 publication, *Advances*. In 1996 Congress increased by 7.1 percent the funding for the National Institute on Aging (which provides over half of all the National Institutes of Health funds devoted to AD research). That was encouraging, but compared to the $5.6 billion allotted for cancer, HIV/AIDS, and heart research, the $323 million budgeted in 1997 for Alzheimer's seems woefully inadequate. The Alzheimer's Association remains the largest private funder of AD research. A hopeful sign of progress is the Ronald and Nancy Reagan Research Institute, which emphasizes intervention before someone with the disease shows symptoms. The institute is now providing an international link to researchers globally.

At the time of Mother's diagnosis, I was driven by fear. For years she had told and retold the story of her mother, who had become senile. One day, after being discovered naked under the dining room table, my grandmother was taken to the state hospital, where she died several years later. Depression settled in and I began monitoring myself for lapses in memory. I was rewarded with a number of startling incidents that convinced me I was already starting to "get it."

I went to my doctor. He laughed. "Don't be silly. Everyone has lapses of memory. You'll be in your eighties and still worrying about getting Alzheimer's disease." Finding this response unhelpful, I went to see a counselor friend whose mother had just died in a nursing home from complications of "probable Alzheimer's disease." She listened. She quietly pointed out the unhappy results of living with such a sense of panic and constant watchfulness over every encounter. Then she directed my focus toward the positive things I could do to help my father. (Eight years later, a social worker listened carefully to my description of my parents' needs. Then, with cocked head and raised eyebrow, she scrutinized my face and said, "You know, they say this disease is genetic." I nodded. She persisted. "It even hits people in their forties and fifties!" "Yes, I know." I still shudder as I remember the impact these careless comments had on me before I came to terms with the genetic implications of this disease.)

I began to share with Dad, as much as possible, the significant and helpful suggestions I was able to glean. The primary task at first, however, was to provide him with situations where we could talk freely about the problem. During my visits we golfed, shopped, or raked leaves, but seldom did he bring up the subject. Interestingly, Mother sought the privacy of moments apart to talk about her failing memory, but always with the admonition not to worry Charles about it. She was deeply depressed.

Ours was a family, not untypical, which had always protected the younger generation from bad news. It seems to come from a mixture of pride in being able to handle difficulties and a genuine concern for not wanting to worry others. Many families play this hide-and-seek game of avoiding discussion of the problem among one another or close friends. Perhaps for some it is a helpful form of temporary protection. The reality of facing this disease is so overwhelming that one tends to do anything to avoid confronting it, hoping it may be something else and will get better. What would better serve both the afflicted loved one and the caregiver is to learn what drugs are available and effective for use in the early stages of AD.

## DRUG STUDIES, GENETICS, FAITH

It is difficult to write about available drugs, drugs in the testing phase, or genetic studies, as changes appear on the horizon with some regularity, outdating prior modes of thinking and treating this disease. Latest international research seems to indicate that cigarette smoking may increase one's chances of developing AD. Drugs are being developed, tested, and marketed as possible treatments for AD.

Early inquiry is important. Very soon, drugs may become available that could delay onset of this disease. According to the director of the Ronald and Nancy Reagan Research Institute, a five-year delay in onset of symptoms could cut in half the number of people affected with AD. In 1996 such a goal seemed within reach. At present, a few available drugs show signs of slowing down the progression of the disease for some people.

Work is being done on testing the slowing of cognitive decline through use of nonsteroidal anti-inflammatory drugs, antioxidants such as *Ginkgo biloba*, vitamin E, estrogen-replacement therapy, and many other kinds of research efforts. A growing number of drug trials are being launched, which may be a possible option for your loved one to try. Contact the Alzheimer's Association at 800-272-3900 and ask for the latest information on drug research and trials. If you should decide, along with your physician, to try one of the drugs now available, the caregiver and afflicted loved one should have an open discussion with the doctor about the possible benefits, risks, side effects, and cost of taking the drug.

At the writing of this revised edition in 1998, family history and genotype are not certain predictors regarding Alzheimer's disease. The general wisdom remains for now that no new treatments have resulted from genetic research. And though the whole area of drug treatments and genetics seems to be exploding with possibility, there is nothing at present you can do or avoid to change your risk of AD.[2] A study referred to as "the nuns study" observed that nuns who regularly exercise their minds through leisure and educational activities were more likely to live free from dementia longer than those who did not engage in these activities. It has also been noted that people who are physically active seem to maintain cognitive function at higher levels longer. For more information about drug therapies used as AD progresses, see chapter 7.

Two articles in the spring 1998 issue of *The Caregiver,* the newsletter of the Duke Family Support Program, indicate researchers are discovering that regular church attendance and religious faith impact the immune system, speeding recovery from depression and maintaining good health in general. As you will see, attending church not only provided our family with a link to something deep and long lasting with Mother, it also kept Dad anchored to the faith he had always practiced with her among their worshiping friends.

One courageous couple, upon learning that the wife had AD, decided their friends should know. With encouragement from her husband, the wife called several of their friends to tell them of the diagnosis. Distraught but feeling the strength of shared and informed community, friends and family continue to rally around this couple.

I cannot emphasize strongly enough the value in finding at least one person, preferably several, whom you love and trust enough to speak freely about your worries and fears. Encourage your afflicted loved one to do so as well. At this stage of the disease it is difficult to contemplate one's future. Abiding faith, together with the love and support of family and good friends, can make this pilgrimage less fearful and lonely.

# 2    LEGAL ISSUES

THIS CHAPTER PRIMARILY raises questions you may need to ask and provides examples and resources. As you will see, there are few simple, direct answers. Though the days may seem far away when difficult legal issues will arise for you, resolving these questions as soon as your loved one is diagnosed with Alzheimer's disease will ease later burdens.

With the explosion over health care for the elderly in this country, continuous change in the rules and regulations seems to be the menu for the day. In 1995, seven million Americans sixty-five and older needed long-term care assistance at the cost of $91 billion, according to the General Accounting Office. By 2024 this number is expected to triple. As our government makes promises to relieve the financial burden of citizens faced with catastrophic illness, it's hard to remember *we* are our government. It seems Congress and the Executive Branch move at a snail's pace in effecting change, but we have learned that decisions made in Washington can have unplanned devastating effects on some segments of our population. With increasing powers and funding coming from the state governments, laws among the states vary more and more. A few words of caution: Future changes in the law cannot be predicted. Information gathered here is based on laws in force in 1998 and is subject to change. Therefore, it is important to seek professional advice.

As our population ages, the diseases that cripple are chronic disorders. Consequently, medical diagnoses and procedures are not always particularly helpful. Health insurance and long-term health care insurance are available at significant cost, but some have proposed the need for frailty insurance—private and public—and incentives for early prevention. We need to continue working locally and through our government to achieve creative reforms that go beyond medical needs, to provide support for in-home caregivers, making it possible to keep afflicted loved ones at home as long as possible rather than in nursing homes that Medicare and Medicaid finance at the cost of billions annually. But the government can't do it all, and individuals must prepare early and wisely for the skyrocketing costs of long-term care.

While he was chairman of the U.S. Senate Special Committee on Aging, Sen. John Heinz said in a radio interview, "In this country, it is better to have cancer than Alzheimer's Disease. We pay for treatment of cancer, but with AD, you are on your own and out of luck."

Dr. Miriam Aronson, professor of neurology at the Albert Einstein College of Medicine, observed that patients do as well as the family does. She remarked, "If caregivers in this country went on strike, the national entitlement system would be bankrupt in one day."

A certified elder law attorney speaking to the local AD support group described the enormous and ever increasing financial pressures on the national care systems. Private insurers are switching to managed care and wielding arbitrary decisions about individuals' health care as ordered by their personal physicians. These decisions many times relate to government programs like Medicare, which is now managed by private insurers who are constantly squeezing costs with an eye on the bottom line. "People show me out-of-date books they've used thinking their legal matters are all in order, but things have changed, and for some it can be too late to do the best kind of planning. The best legal advice I can give you is to get legal advice *early* from an elder law attorney. Trying to understand the rules which are constantly changing is like going to the Mad Hatter's tea party. Good sense does not necessarily apply."

Yet there are hopeful signs. Thanks to federal grants and many hardworking people, some states are successfully developing a cadre of health care volunteers, trained at no cost to participants, in churches and community centers. This free training is offered in return for two to four hours per week of in-home care to families who need help. It's an exciting concept, but volunteers will not solve this problem.

The Older Americans Act Amendments of 1984 called for community-based, long-term care services, demonstration projects, and training of professional caregivers.[1] State legislatures are slowly moving toward funding services to provide the "best possible care in the least restrictive environment" (in-home). The Alzheimer's Association reported in their November 1997 *Public Policy Update* that Congress is finally recognizing the needs of persons with chronic illness and disability, including those with AD, as having a place in Medicare's future. In the 1997 Balanced Budget Act, a mandate was given to the commission on the future of Medicare to consider the impact of chronic illness on costs and quality of care.[2] Yet we've seen the work of numerous commissions named to study a problem shelved in the heat of congressional debate. Progress toward this goal is still in the early stages, so the admonition to plan ahead even before diagnosis is relevant for all.

At a meeting of my AD support group, a white-haired, gentle-speaking man approached me during our coffee time. "All this talk about legal planning makes me uneasy. Somehow it seems devious. All our lives my wife and I have done without fancy vacations, big homes, expensive restaurants, and the like to save our money so we could have a secure and comfortable old age together. Now I'm beginning to get the message that because she has AD, we should 'protect our assets,' which sounds like devising legal means to hide what money we have." He was quite disturbed at the thought. He frowned, his blue eyes clouded as he shook his head. "It doesn't seem honest to me."

Nevertheless, present governmental policies aiming for "fiscal responsibility" force AD families, especially, into taking a hard look at their financial picture, present and future, and making big decisions. For most middle-income citizens who need extended care, the cost may well eventually deplete your assets, which makes planning so essential. No matter what the average annual cost of nursing home care is (approximately $43,000 per year in 1998) your planning must investigate the cost per year, including projected costs, in your area. They vary widely. For example, in 1998 in Fairfield County, Connecticut, annual nursing home costs run from $72,000 to $108,000; in the Florida Keys, $35,000 to $42,000; in North Carolina, $36,000 to $72,000. It all depends on the services provided and location. Generally speaking, no matter where you live, if you're approaching retirement years with a modest nest egg, the choices hang heavy over your "golden years."

It is necessary to understand that at this writing, Medicare, federally funded and administered, is an acute-care medical health insurance primarily for people over sixty-five. Regulations are uniform across the country. On the other hand, Medicaid, one of the most complex laws of the United States, is a welfare program. It is a federal/state-funded and state-administered program of assistance, not an insurance program or entitlement. Regulations vary from state to state, and each state interprets the law somewhat differently.

In seeking information, I called three different Medicaid offices. In the first call, I received no clear, direct answers; those came from the second call. From the third, I received not only helpful information, but also an offer to seek more complete answers and the promise of a return call. However, I didn't get the call. Lesson? Don't give up after one call.

As I interviewed people and met with small groups, I heard the same questions repeatedly. I took my questions to state Departments on Aging, the local Department on Aging, Medicaid offices, the Internal Revenue Service, the Alzheimer's Association, the United Seniors Health Cooperative, and the Duke Family Support Program, part of Duke Medical Center. I talked to lawyers, read elder law newsletters, and attended AD support groups where attorneys spoke on matters of assistance for the aging. Questions, with the best answers I could find, follow.

*How can an older person best obtain legal advice and assistance?* Preferably one should look for a lawyer who specializes in probate and elder law. You can locate a certified elder law attorney nearest you by calling the National Academy of Elder Law Attorneys at 520-881-4005. These lawyers work with guardianship and disability planning, estate planning, medical care decision making, long-term care issues, Medicaid and Medicare, as well as other areas of law that impact older adults.

Frequently, attorneys who provide legal services for the poor have had experience with government programs. If you do not know an attorney experienced in these areas, check with local agencies to obtain good quality local referrals. These might be the Alzheimer's Association, AARP, your local Legal Aid Society or area Department on Aging, your hospital, or a nursing home social services department. Your state or county bar association lawyer referral service will send a list of attorneys practicing elder law. People in your local AD support group have legal contacts and the stories to go along with them about their experience with certain lawyers. You should receive several references. Call each reference and inquire about the length of the lawyer's experience with the legalities of estate planning, problems of aging, and Medicaid laws and what percentage of his or her practice is devoted to these areas. Do not be shy or hesitant to ask whether there is a fee for the first consultation, how much it is, and an approximate length of time the work should take. Be sure to ask what information you need to bring with you.

In addition to the above sources, you might contact your state Department on Aging and its local offices. Some towns make free legal services available to senior citizens on a monthly basis at the local senior center. An individual with a limited income may obtain services from the local State Legal Services office, or your local Legal Aid Society, which renders free legal help to the poor. Income restrictions, however, are severe. Nearby university law schools often offer public legal assistance. The Institute of Certified Financial Planners at 800-282-7526 can provide names of members who work in a specific region and specialize in assisting people with serious illnesses. State your age and the age of your spouse, and identify yourself as the caregiver of an individual afflicted with AD. Be sure to state that you need to know what to do to protect your finances.

Do not put off making this contact. Unpleasant though it may be to the afflicted person, lawyers regularly meet with clients who are in the early stages of AD to establish powers of attorney for both financial and health care decisions. If you are a person diagnosed with Alzheimer's disease, cooperating with consulting a lawyer is a great gift you can give your caregiver to ease the way as you face a difficult future together.

*Who may act on behalf of AD patients when they become unable to make financial and personal-care decisions? What methods of delegating authority are available?* Many advisers believe the most efficient method for an individual to delegate authority to act is through a durable power of attorney. Through this relatively inexpensive document, the person to whom the power is granted (called the attorney-in-fact) can make decisions for the principal, the individual who has granted the authority to act. At the time of establishing durable power of attorney for business, financial, and personal matters, a living will and power of attorney for health care decisions should also be established. This is especially crucial when there is no close family member. Simply stated, this is legally naming another person to act in one's behalf. It is important to establish backup persons as well.

In some states, the authority of an attorney-in-fact to act ends when the principal becomes incompetent. All states allow for a "durable" power of attorney, under which the authority to act lasts beyond the time of the principal's incompetence and ends at death. The individual who gives authority to another under power of attorney must be competent at the time the document is executed. Therefore, it is extremely important, especially with a person in the early stages of AD, to get these powers established correctly the first time.

A New York elder law attorney suggests that a lawyer or banker also be designated along with an adult child to countersign orders requiring power of attorney. He recommends that this durable power be established routinely along with the writing of one's will.[3]

If the patient has not executed durable and health care powers of attorney and becomes incompetent, the court, upon petition, will appoint judicial officers to make decisions concerning the individual's finances and medical care. In some states, these officers are known as conservators; in other states, they are known as guardians. If a court of law adjudges an individual to be incompetent, that person is legally prohibited from making any decisions, and court-appointed representatives are accountable to the court of appointment for their decisions made on the incompetent person's behalf.

Other people, such as the certified financial planner I consulted with this question, believe that the most efficient method for an individual to delegate authority to act is through a revocable living trust, especially for those who have saved and invested wisely through the years.[4]

While the durable power of attorney is theoretically a valid legal document, it has some drawbacks. The power of attorney is drawn to conform with state law. If an individual becomes a resident of another state, there may be peculiarities of the new state's law that could impede an agent's authority to act. Also, some financial institutions (banks and brokerage firms) will delay a transaction while a power of attorney is reviewed by the corporation's legal counsel. These financial institutions try to get clients to sign a standard power of attorney relating only to the accounts held at the institution. If a "nonstandard" power of attorney is presented to the account manager, the agent may be told that the transaction cannot be completed without significant delay. This presents a major problem if funds are needed immediately, or some other transaction needs to be expedited for the benefit of the client.

The revocable living trust overcomes these problems. Very generally, a revocable living trust is a legal arrangement established by a person (the grantor) during his or her lifetime through which one party (the trustee) holds and manages assets for the benefit of another person (the beneficiary). As its name implies, a revocable living trust may be amended or terminated by the grantor at any time during his or her lifetime.

It is not unusual for one person to play multiple roles in the revocable living trust arrangement. For example, the grantor may also be the trustee and beneficiary until death or incapacity. (Incapacity and how it is to be defined and documented can be written clearly into the language of the trust.) This is referred to as a "self trusteed living trust." After the death or incapacity of the grantor, the named successor trustee assumes the duties of the trust administration. Usually the will is amended to "pour" remaining estate assets into the trust upon the grantor's death. The trust then distributes property to heirs just as the will would have done.

The advantages of the revocable living trust are many. Specifically, you should consider establishing a revocable living trust when you want to:

- Avoid the probate process, including court costs, time delays, and publicity
- Provide for comprehensive management of *all* assets in case of your incapacity
- Provide confidentiality regarding the eventual settlement of your estate
- Provide for immediate distribution of assets to family members or continuing trust arrangements after your death

In a well-crafted estate plan, the power of attorney may be drafted to allow the agent to fund a revocable living trust when the client becomes incapacitated. Then the successor trustee (an individual, a corporate trustee, or a combination of the two in a co-trustee arrangement) may take over the management of the client's assets.

The revocable living trust is easily portable across state lines and most financial institutions will rely on a "trustee certification" as sufficient means to execute transactions. In other words, the trust does not generally have to be reviewed by the bank or brokerage firm.

*Does Medicare pay for the cost of nursing home care? Home health care?*
Medicare's purpose insures only the relatively short-term costs of acute
illness; it does not insure the cost of long-term care. In 1998, Medicare
paid for nursing home care *only if the patient required skilled nursing care.*
The regulatory standards for the condition of a patient needing skilled
nursing care are so strict that few AD patients qualify. Even if a patient
is eligible for skilled nursing care, Medicare's obligation to pay extends
only to one hundred days of care in a skilled nursing facility, preceded
by three *full* days in the hospital. Medicare pays the entire amount for
the first twenty days. For the remaining eighty days, it is a co-payment
arrangement. There is very strong pressure by the system to get people
off Medicare as quickly as possible. This is often accomplished by desig-
nating the patient to a lower level of care; intermediate, for example, after the first twenty days. Thus it is important to know your rights under
the law and to have your doctor in full support of your loved one. If you
feel he or she is being unfairly denied skilled care, contact your doctor. If
your doctor states such services are medically necessary, your loved one
will continue to receive them.[5]

*Is it true that Medicaid is the only government program that pays for ex-
tended skilled or intermediate nursing care and custodial care?* Yes, in
1998. Medicaid is a welfare program that pays for the necessary health
care and long-term care costs of the poor.

*Does a victim of AD have to be nearly penniless before the government will
provide assistance for the costs of long-term care services?* For some, the ultimate expense of nursing home care can be met by income from all
sources—assets, pensions, and Social Security—without leaving the
surviving spouse a pauper. For the wealthy, this can be done by self-in-
suring. For many, it is accomplished only by very careful management at
tremendous financial sacrifice, part of which may include the cost of
long-term health care insurance (see chap. 8). One state welfare official
told me, "You are penalized for having saved and rewarded for having
spent it all." Bottom line, someone has to pay the cost. It's true, either
each family bears the financial burden or we share it with our friends,
neighbors, and all other taxpayers. But fraud, abuse, and mismanage-
ment have added enormously to the burden of cost.

Passage of the Medicare Catastrophic Coverage Act of 1988 dealt with the problem of "spousal impoverishment" of the well spouse by the overwhelming cost of long-term care for the ill spouse. Nationwide this act allows the well spouse to retain one-half of all the available assets up to a federally established maximum, which leaves that spouse with what Congress considers an adequate, but not luxurious, income. Somewhat complicated calculations are used to make the determination of what and how much income and assets the well spouse may hold, and the formulas vary from state to state. All this must be looked at when Medicaid becomes involved as well.

*If the AD patient is married, does the marital home have to be sold and the proceeds expended for the patient's care before the patient becomes eligible for Medicaid?* As stated above, regulations vary from state to state. Almost universally among the states, the answer is no. For example, in Florida in 1998 the home is not counted if the individual's spouse or dependent relative is living there. Burial funds up to $2,500 and one car are also excluded. The well spouse may continue to reside in the home until death or until it is vacated.

"Under federal law, states *must* recover against the probate estate (property passing under a will) of a deceased Medicaid recipient. States *may* recover against any other assets that the deceased recipient held an interest in at time of death. This covers all assets not in the probate estate... to include property owned with a right of survivorship, property in certain trusts, insurance proceeds, retirement death benefits and life estates."[6]

In some states, upon death of the well spouse, funds realized from the sale of the house go to the state that has paid or is paying, through Medicaid, for nursing home care for the sick spouse. In other states, should the marital home be in the joint names of the spouses, a lien is placed against the applicant spouse's interest and the value is paid to the state upon its sale. As such legalities and variations differ from state to state, sound legal advice can prevent assets from being wasted before applying for Medicaid and can preserve assets for the benefit of the surviving spouse.

*What happens to cash savings and other liquid assets titled in the joint names of the spouses? In the sole name of the AD patient? In the sole name of the well spouse?* In every state nearly all of the liquid assets titled in the sole name of the AD patient must be spent for his or her care before Medicaid eligibility begins. But it becomes complex. In some states the AD patient becomes eligible for Medicaid when one half of the couple's total assets and income are expended for his or her care. The remaining half is then considered the separate share of the well spouse, who is not required to pay for the care of the spouse eligible for Medicaid. However, other states require that the combined assets and income of husband and wife must be used to pay for the institutional care of the ill spouse, allowing the well spouse only a capped amount of income on which to live. For example, in Florida in 1998 the well spouse, in addition to the home and car, is "allocated $80,760 of the combined value of the total countable resources."[7] This income limit is adjusted in January of each year based on cost-of-living increases.

Some lawyers advise older couples to transfer their jointly owned assets, or assets owned solely by the ill spouse, to the well spouse. This must be done with great care. In states with shorter preapplication divestiture time, this may preserve the married couple's property without affecting medical assistance eligibility. However, these "look-back" divestiture times are being extended in many states. In Florida, Connecticut, and North Carolina transfer of assets cannot take place within thirty-six months (three full years) of application for Medicaid. The state looks back sixty months (five full years) on the establishment of trusts upon Medicaid application. It is crucial the application not be made before these time restrictions are met, as penalties are significant.

"Gifting of assets . . . to family members is at once the most obvious and most problematic approach," writes Michael Gilfix, a California attorney who specializes in gerontological law. "There can be no strings attached. An 'understanding' that money will be kept for the impaired person's spouse is not and cannot be binding." Besides adding stress to an already stressful family situation, such gifting "can result in a determination of *ineligibility* for Medicaid, if done inexpertly."[8]

Opinions vary. Ellice Fatoullah, a New York City elder law attorney, and David E. Fraser recommend that "the easiest and least costly means of money management is the outright gift—a course generally recommended for patients with less than $50,000 in assets." Of course the burden of taxes falls on the recipient of such gifts, and there exists the opportunity for mismanagement of such transferred assets.[9]

To make certain both spouses are properly protected, an elder law attorney or a competent financial adviser should carefully review any estate-planning technique to pay for the cost of long-term care.

*Are the adult children of a parent receiving Medicaid required to contribute to the financial support of that parent?* While some states excuse adult children from the responsibility of having to financially support a parent receiving Medicaid, other states do require adult children to pay a monthly amount for the support of a parent receiving medical assistance.

*What must the current asset amount of the estate be to qualify for Medicaid?* Medicaid is funded roughly half by the federal government and half by the states and is administered by the states following federal guidelines. Some federal laws are mandatory, some allow each state to choose which rules they will implement. Some states have restrictive income limitations, others don't. Some states allow spouses to retain more assets than others, and states have different exempt assets and different rules for determining whether an asset, such as a home, qualifies. Given a certain level of assets, you could be eligible in one state but ineligible in another. For all practical purposes, the assets limitations are severe, with modest allowance set aside for funeral expenses. California adopted legislation calling for the Department of Health to inform newly admitted nursing home patients of their right to "separation of community property." This means that a couple can separate jointly owned assets into two equal shares. The stricken spouse can then "spend down" to become eligible for Medicaid. The spouse remaining at home still has half their assets. However, the couple must make this contract before the impaired spouse is unable to sign, unless they have established durable power of attorney.

*In addition to Medicaid, what other sources help pay nursing home cost?* When a person becomes eligible for Medicaid upon admission to a nursing home or while in a nursing home, all states require that Social Security payments, pensions, and any other disability income the patient may receive must be paid to the institution rendering the care services. The AD-afflicted husband of one woman I interviewed had been a fireman and received no Social Security. The cost of nursing home care consumed all their assets. His pension check was going directly to the nursing home. Her only income—about one third of his pension check—was doled out to her by the nursing home until legal assistance managed to have his check redirected to her. She spoke of the relief this singular change brought in her meager life as we sat together in the nursing home, where she goes daily to feed her husband and others, some of whom sit restrained in docile, medicated silence, staring at a TV. Her children are now supporting her.

*Does Medicaid offer any assistance for the cost of such things as in-home health care, adult day care, or respite care?* In a growing number of states a Medicaid waiver may be requested for custodial care. I visited the local Department of Children and Families in Florida with questions about Medicaid. I was treated with courtesy and given easy-to-read copies of the July 1995 "Medicaid Summary of Services," which includes home and community-based waiver services. (Six Medicaid waivers are available in Florida.)

Based on the federal Omnibus Reconciliation Act of 1981, which was designed to help people remain in their homes, these home and community-based services "waive federal requirements to allow states to provide home and community-based services to individuals who would require institutionalization without these services." Each state legislature must design its own specific package for target groups. Florida has three waivers serving "individuals...at risk of placement in a skilled or intermediate nursing home."[10] Other sections of the Medicaid laws they provided about these matters clearly explained the conditions of meeting Medicaid eligibility. It becomes obvious that for each family circumstance the answers to these questions will vary somewhat.

Contact your local Medicaid office, the welfare agency in your state, or the area Agency on Aging (federal program), and ask if they have any special waiver to include these services. The state must be able to show that the cost for these services is equal to or less than the cost of nursing home care. The Office of Management and Budget under the Health Care Finance Administration/Department of Health and Human Services in Hyattsville, Maryland, has information about Medicaid waivers. They can also tell you if your state has such waivers available to you. They recommend that if you are paying for your spouse's care, record everything expended for caregiving. Keep track of every penny spent. The better documented and organized your records, the less your record keeping will be questioned. If you are refused any available Medicaid assistance and feel you are qualified, you have the right to appeal. Do not hesitate to do so.[11]

*What source of income is available to a wife who has never worked and whose husband is a patient in a nursing home where he receives Medicaid?* Depending upon the age, health, and family situation of the wife, she may be entitled to receive general assistance from AFDC (Aid for Dependent Children) from her state's welfare department. She may also sue her husband for support while he is in a nursing home. Filed by her lawyer, this court order of support provides for the husband's income to support the wife rather than its being spent by the nursing home.

The wife is not eligible to receive Social Security under these circumstances until her sixty-second birthday. At that time she receives about one-half of her husband's Social Security.

*Are there any tax deductions for a person paying the entire cost of either day/in-home health care or nursing home care for an afflicted person needing custodial care?* The Economic Recovery Act of 1982 permits a federal tax credit to families in all tax brackets with elderly dependents who attend out-of-home adult day-care centers.

In 1998, those who paid for nursing home care could figure 7.5 percent of their adjusted gross income, subtract that amount from the cost of the nursing home care, and deduct the remainder. However, a taxpayer would be wise to consult with a tax attorney or accountant to determine his or her entitlement to this deduction, as the deductibility of nursing home care and in-home health care is governed by Internal Revenue Service regulations, which change at an astonishing pace. At this writing, *qualified* expenses for long-term care are deductible. Generally, this means medical or skilled nursing care. Careful documentation must be made. (See pp. 71–73, "Long-Term Care Insurance.")

*Is the AD patient entitled to disability or other benefits if he or she is unable to continue working?* An individual younger than sixty-five and diagnosed with AD may be eligible for disability benefits through Social Security. Application should be made immediately upon diagnosis, as there is a delay before the benefits begin. This is done at your local Social

Security office. If you think you may be entitled to a benefit, don't just ask if you can get it. File an application. Make sure you have your birth certificate or other proof of birth date, marriage license, and your Social Security card. If you have a Social Security number but have lost your card, apply for a new card, but not a new number. The Social Security Administration can probably find your number. Give them a call.

The government's criterion for disability is that the applicant is totally unable to work at any job at all. Because of this strict criterion, Social Security claims representatives will sometimes deny benefits to a patient in the early or middle stages of the disease process. However, an appeal of a denial of benefits to an administrative law judge is frequently successful. Do not be afraid to appeal—more than once if necessary. By reason of the employment contract, some employees are covered by a company or union disability insurance plan. These benefits should be examined and considered before the employee accepts early retirement or another type of mutual and voluntary termination of employment because of Alzheimer's disease.

If the employee does not qualify for disability benefits, he or she may be entitled to receive unemployment compensation on the basis of inability to maintain his or her present job for medical reasons.

The AD patient's family could also check whether disability benefits are available through state or city government. It is worth noting the following helpful information about insurance published by the Alzheimer's Association newsletter of the Chicago chapter:

> If you are paying premiums on a life insurance policy for one who is suffering from AD, check your policy to see if it contains a waiver of premium rider. If it does, this [can] mean that when this person is no longer able to perform customary work or duties, you do not have to make this premium payment. All other aspects of the policy remain the same. Cash value is not affected, you may still borrow against the policy, and the death value remains the same. You simply do not have to pay any more premiums. If you have been paying on such a policy, it is usually possible to contact your insurance agent or the company directly and request a refund. Call your life insurance company for details. If a policy is missing, you can have it traced by writing to The Institute of Life Insurance for a missing policy questionnaire. They will circulate

the information to the 150 largest insurance companies. Write to: Policy Search Department, RAI, American Council of Life Insurance, 1850 K Street N.W., Washington, DC 20006.[12]

*Is the AD patient eligible for help through the Veterans Administration?* The Veterans Administration provides long-term care through its national system of hospitals for honorably discharged veterans. Under federal law, eligibility and access to the veterans hospitals for the veteran suffering from a nonservice-connected disability are determined by several criteria in a priority ranking that includes age and financial status. VA hospital services are free to veterans.

The U.S. government is not expanding the number of nursing beds in VA hospitals, even though the number of disabled veterans requiring these services is rapidly increasing. Custodial care units in VA hospitals are limited and the waiting lists are long. Thus, many disabled veterans are being excluded from institutional services.

The legal complexities and necessary decisions for financial estate planning and management are serious challenges for a person not accustomed to such matters. Even the caregiver experienced and prepared to make these decisions finds it a difficult task. The effect of facing such a grim future with the indescribable heartache of seeing a beloved spouse deteriorating into a state of total helplessness can deplete the initiative needed to address these vital matters carefully, thoughtfully, and soon enough.

For the caregiver who has never worked in business or participated in family financial planning, the decisions posed by legalities may bring about emotional paralysis. This is the time when legal counsel can be a tremendous help. Keep in mind that laws and regulations vary from state to state and are subject to change at any time. With our population aging and pressure on Congress and state legislatures building, laws affecting the elderly will be in the process of change for many years. *As soon as possible upon diagnosis,* seek the best professional counsel available to you, whether through public agencies or private attorneys. This enables the caregiver to tend to financial estate and personal care planning and management and to prepare as thoroughly as possible for the long road ahead.[13]

# 3  PROGRESSIVE STAGES

Positive identification of any individual case of AD by stages is nearly impossible. Though understood to be problematic, staging is merely a way for medical people, writers, and families to write, study, and speak about the progression of this deteriorating disease. For example, Mother, in the eleventh year since we first noticed symptoms, is still able to eat in a restaurant and feed herself with some help. She is beginning to have speech and occasional incontinence problems. For others, feeding, speech, and continence capability are lost early.

For some of us who give care, it seems helpful to be able to identify the stage our loved one is passing through. I recognize it in myself—this need to know. I was struck by this thought while visiting a Catholic church recently, where I observed people as they moved through the Stations of the Cross. There is some elusive satisfaction in being able to say, "Yes, this is where we've been; this is where we are now." It's like finding a familiar peg in a dark hallway.

The prognosis for estimating how long one may suffer with this disease is also difficult. There does seem to be some evidence that the younger the age of onset, the more rapid the decline.[1] However, this quickened unfolding of the disease process is generally true of most diseases that strike at an early age. Make no hasty assumptions; this is not inevitable. Some people seem to plateau at different times and maintain a certain degree of stability or arrested decline. These plateaus, too, are as unpredictable as duration. For some it is over within three years after onset. For others, like Mother, the loss is extremely gradual and can continue some fifteen years (medical diagnosis, with considerable accuracy, now places the disease in the early middle stages).[2] Researchers, believing that the disease begins to attack the brain thirty to forty years before symptoms appear, are hard at work on technologies for early detection to permit testing of preventative treatments *before* symptoms develop at the expected age of onset.

Although usually able to continue a fairly normal life for some time, some AD sufferers remain outwardly cheerful, while others become irritable or depressed. In an Oregon chapter Alzheimer's Association newsletter, a person asked about depression and boredom: "My father just sits around and stares, looks out the window but never speaks. Should I try to get him interested in something new?" Benson Schaeffer, psychologist, counseled: "What is for us a reasonable variety of [stimuli] is, for persons with AD, too much, too quickly. [They] need...much more time to process and react to fewer and much simpler events... help him continue doing the things he can, however small and dull [they] seem to you.... Your unhappiness may be his serenity."[3]

Gradual impairment of understanding, reasoning, and ability to use good judgment may bring changes in personality. Sometimes lifelong personality patterns are increasingly exaggerated. Mother's normally easy and outgoing personality evolved into one of placid withdrawal. Not until nine to ten years into the disease did she begin to display hostile and aggressive behavior. In other instances personalities can change drastically early on.

One wife, whose husband is now in a nursing home, told me, "For a while I couldn't understand how God could let such a thing happen. This man who would never even kill a fly now sometimes smacked me 'til I was black and blue. I had many a black eye! I got through it by reminding myself how it would kill him if he knew what he was doing. I remember my mother told me, 'No matter how bad off you are, there's always someone worse off. As long as you have your health, you're rich. So you keep your faith and count on it to make you strong enough to get through.' Those words helped me make it."

The ability to perform sequential tasks—financial planning, meal planning, home repairs—becomes severely impaired. The gradual loss of lifelong skills such as driving, keeping a checkbook, and counting money comes as a blow to both the afflicted and the caregiver. In some cases neglect of good personal hygiene is a startling offense to family and friends. Special sensitivity is needed to maintain dignity and avoid hostility (see chap. 7). Encourage continued participation in decision making, treatment, and planning for the future.

Though Mother gave up driving without much resistance after she became lost downtown, finally finding her way home after hours of anguished attempts, for many this loss is severe and angrily denied. If you observe driving patterns changing, difficulty remembering how to get places, failure to mind regulation signs, speeding, becoming angry or confused at the wheel, or forgetting where they are going, it's time to draw the line and face this problem together. Ask the doctor to talk to your loved one about not driving and to write a prescription that reads, "No Driving." Reassure your loved one that you will make arrangements for transportation whenever he or she needs to go somewhere. Don't be shy about asking friends and family to help with this. Park the car out of sight, and, if necessary, disable it. For a while this may cause depression and hostility. Firmly explain that you understand how difficult this is, but don't let it become a focus of argument. You might ask a close friend of the afflicted or even your insurance agent to explain the dangers and necessity of this move.

Adaptation to these losses differs in as many ways as there are families who suffer them. We went through all of the following: bewilderment at what was happening and what to do about it; focusing on the lost capacities; rage at the time we spent finding misplaced items; overwhelming grief and frustration at the enormity of the problem and the lack of workable solutions or hope for reprieve; insidious fear that "I may get it, too"; overprotection of the afflicted to spare embarrassment; not talking much about the problem with each other or with friends; depression on the part of the afflicted, the caregiver, and close family members; isolation as friends avoid coming to visit; confused feelings of hate and love for the afflicted one, which are the beginnings of separation; anger at being stuck with such an unrelenting burden; guilt at having all these feelings about someone we love. It's a big bundle we carry.

What are some of the practical things to do to help make life bearable? Address the problems openly with the afflicted person and with other family members. As a family, expect to feel grief and allow yourself to share it. This does not mean that you cry on every shoulder available.

First there is a grief to be shared between the two of you, if possible. If the words are impossible, a silent but receptive embrace can fulfill a need that is greater than the need to talk and can transmit the understood and felt sorrow. If you have neglected this means of communication, nurture it; it will serve you both in the long days ahead.

Include the children and encourage them to raise their questions and fears about how this disease may change the way a grandparent (or parent) is able to relate to them. The simple gestures of love and affection that children so spontaneously offer can be more healing than anything we attempt to devise. Make it clear that it is "our" problem and we face it together.

When AD is finally diagnosed (and this may legitimately take a period of some months), begin to educate yourself about the disease. Contact the national Alzheimer's Association (see p. 140, "Helpful Resources") and become an informed supporter of the work they do. They will send you information on local chapters along with informative brochures on particular problems. Look for AD support groups near you. Check hospitals, visiting nurse associations, and public health departments such as the local Department of Aging in your town. If your area has an "Info Line," call it for any information related to AD. If there is no AD support group near you, consider starting one. Your church could be instrumental in helping you.

There is something strengthening in being able to name one's enemy and confront it. When you can gather the courage to locate and attend some of these meetings, you will find yourself in the company of heroes. You'll learn from them even as you reveal your own anguish, and in doing so you will become one of them. Kathy Eddy, in the beautiful book she and her photographer husband, Robert, created for caregivers, writes: "Our own acquaintance with grief informs our caregiving. The pain we have known sensitizes us to the suffering of others and increases our capacity for compassion and loving service a hundredfold. When we have known the utterly dependable presence of God in times of grief and despair, we have an invaluable gift to offer others."[4]

Your AD support group is the place to talk about your problems with those who suffer as you do. It is the place to ask, "How did you manage when...? What do you do about...? Are you still able to...? Where did you find help with...?" This in itself helps alleviate many of the conflicting feelings of helplessness, hopelessness, guilt, and anger. At the same time, it helps you become informed of the newest research and developing treatments.

It is the opinion of a New York City therapist who works primarily with families of AD sufferers that her first task is to help them recognize their denial (usually at work in both the caregiver and the afflicted person). Her next challenge is to help them accept the reality of this life-changing tragedy and then start grappling with the job of detachment—of letting go.

"I sometimes feel there is a degree of selfishness in keeping the afflicted person at home longer than is meaningful, because it gives focus and meaning to the caregiver's life," she said. Obviously, her work is with caregivers and her concern lies with them, helping them maintain involvement with life and living. Yet I believe this apparent "hanging on," this continued commitment, can also be understood differently for the person who has lived a lifetime with the instruction to "love one another as I have loved you. No one has greater love than this, to lay down one's life for one's friends" (John 15:13). In any case, where love is still alive, letting go is a long, hard, gradual process. An AD support group can help you make this pilgrimage.

Remind yourself daily that many of the peculiar things your loved one says and does are out of his or her control. It is the result of damage within the brain. It was a big step when my father finally realized this and stopped angrily accusing Mother of not concentrating or not trying hard enough to remember something. This step is not achieved by an intellectual decision. It is a growing awareness that finally settles in to stay.

A friend who has two sisters with AD attended a meeting of parish clergy, physicians, and hospital chaplains. All of them were describing their feelings of inadequacy and helplessness when an AD-afflicted patient confronted them. "I was astonished at how little they knew about responding to both the afflicted person and the caregiver," she reported in dismay. "Finally, I suggested it was my experience that the best thing I can do for my sisters is to pet them, hug them, touch them in ways that convey my love for them." (See "Helpful Resources" section for "You Are One of Us" booklet.)

A St. Louis Alzheimer's Association newsletter had this to say about the value of communicating through touching:

Sensations from the skin are apparently represented by a large area of the brain and therefore stand more chance of "getting through." The victim often interprets lack of touching as a personal and social rejection. By using this means of communication you are helping to reduce the feelings of confusion and insecurity as well as increasing understanding between you. This kind of communication occurs on conscious and unconscious levels and touching becomes a very important tool to remember. Use it to gain attention and keep the person listening to you. It shows that the loved one is worthy of care and reduces feelings of isolation and rejection in both of you. Touching increases interaction between you, lets the other know you are listening, and reinforces trust at a level s/he will be able to understand.[5]

Having said all this, I learned from one man in our support group that his wife resents being touched. Doing so can even provoke violent behavior. Conversations with nursing home staff who work with AD patients confirm this opposing reality—another example of the unpredictability inherent in this disease process.

Use the time of these early middle stages to explore memories of the past. These memories are heightened and often clear. Document family history. Talk together on a tape recorder about pictures, old pieces of family furniture or china, important incidents, and events in the person's past.

I recall with delight doing this with Mother. At first she was shy about speaking into the small mike, but our conversation was easy and she soon overcame that. She began telling stories; some I had heard long ago, others were new to me. We wandered into the living room and talked about pieces of china and glassware in the corner cupboard. I heard again the cherished story of the tall, blue glass pitcher her father had chosen while he was away on his first cattle roundup to Dodge City, Kansas, soon after his marriage. He had tied the delicate pitcher to his saddle and returned to his bride with this sparkling sky-blue gift.

As she spoke, I noticed a handful of broken pottery and shards of glass in the bottom of a bowl. I asked what they could possibly be. Immediately I heard a story that would never have been told had we not spent this time together. These were remains she had discovered on her last trip to her home in Kansas, at the site of the "soddy" where her grandparents had first lived. One of the broken pieces could well have been part of the handle to the blue willowware sugar bowl from a tea service we later discovered behind the chimney in the attic (see "I Hear the Sights of Things," pp. 120–21 in the "Poems" section). It was a bittersweet day, a day I will always cherish as a gift of time.

# 4 MAINTAINING COMMUNICATION

Be generous with your friends. Understand that their seeming neglect results mostly from mistrust of their own sense of knowing how to respond to their afflicted friend and to you. The grim reality they see when they are with you forces them to struggle with fears about their own death and dying. When they ask, be specific about what they can do. In general, that includes doing anything with their afflicted friend, either in the home or outside, which frees you to leave and do something you need or want to do. The following few paragraphs are directed to such friends and neighbors who want to help.

All these activities are possibilities for a friend to do with an afflicted person: going out to lunch; window shopping; shopping for specific items, such as women's underwear, which is difficult for most men; visiting an old friend, a park, or a museum; going to the grocery store (provide a shopping list), post office, hairdresser, or movie; looking at postcards, family pictures, or slides; and reading to one another.

When cooking, keep your friend and caregiver in mind. Package an extra amount in a freezer container and drop it by. When planning to shop, call the caregiver and ask if anything is needed. Ask for a list of chores he or she finds difficult to get to and give some regular time to accomplishing those. Invite the couple to your home for a meal or out to a restaurant (private rooms can be arranged if it would be more comfortable to do so), or to a park for a picnic. If the ill spouse cannot function in such a setting, arrange for a sitter and take the caregiver out for a meal.

If you are a reasonably healthy retired person, find the caregiver of a mentally impaired loved one and volunteer some time regularly with them. My widowed mother-in-law has shown me the beauty of such caring on those occasions when my parents visited. Although she is a semi-invalid, her ability to be present with Mother and to keep track of her was a great help to my father and me. But more than that, the camaraderie between her and my father filled an empty place in both their lives.

While visiting Mother several years ago, she insisted on "helping." Out of exasperation I asked her to read to me while I prepared dinner. I chose several copies of *Guideposts* magazine primarily because the stories were short and the pictures plentiful. Mother had trouble knowing what to do at the end of a column. She often got lost or began over again at the top of the page. Nonetheless, her pleasure in reading to me was tremendous. I asked her several days later if she'd like to read to me from a book I had brought along to read myself. The story was a simple fantasy symbolic of life's struggle with good and evil. We sat together for a half hour or so at a time. She read several times a day for the rest of my visit. By the time I left, she seemed to be recognizing the names of the major characters (which were unusual and highly amusing), and she turned the pages herself in anticipation of what was to come.

Music and movement are universal languages the mentally impaired can enjoy long after reason and memory have been destroyed. On that same visit, Mother and I spent several evenings dancing to music on tape or radio. Her pleasure in both the movement and the physical touching brought smiles I hadn't seen in several years.

A neurologist friend tells about a patient, mute and withdrawn for some time, who responded to music with movement and obvious pleasure. We who give care feel joy when we see such a response. Silent withdrawal troubles us. It is the opinion of Dr. Barry Reisberg, a noted authority on AD, that such withdrawal compensates for decreasing mental capacities, thus reducing anxiety. It is a form of protection.[1]

Music was always a special part of Mother's life. Years before all this began, I remember her requesting that we have the Hallelujah Chorus from Handel's *Messiah* played or sung at her funeral. Seeing her now move into this protective withdrawal was sad for us. At Dad's birthday celebration I placed headsets on each of them and turned on a tape of the Hallelujah Chorus. Her body straightened; her eyes lit up. She raised her hands and began to move them, singing with the music. For some moments she was lost in the music, totally absorbed. Dad watched her face in a glowing wonder. For a few short months, this means of reconnecting was helpful. But soon her ability to enjoy it was gone, and she no longer had patience with the headset.

A member of my support group said recently, "I'm so thankful for jigsaw puzzles! Bill spends hours at them. He's so patient figuring them out. The other day when I paused to look over his shoulder to see how he was doing, he asked, 'Don't you have something else to do?' The doctor says he can still do this because apparently the part of his brain that determines spatial perception has not yet been affected. He can still play cards, too... even bridge. But he can't remember to put milk on his cereal, or the names of our grandchildren, or what day or year it is. He keeps his journal every night, and seems to enjoy that." Other members of the group were quite amazed. Experiences with their loved ones were quite different.

Small tasks, such as sorting things—nuts, bolts, washers, screws, poker chips, marbles, neckties, jewelry, buttons, socks—or picking sunflower seeds out of a bag of birdseed, shining shoes, sanding wood, or even listening to books on tape keep a loved one stimulated, occupied, and feeling useful.

Don't overlook pet therapy. The calming effect of stroking and loving a pet is for some a nonthreatening source of great comfort. For those who exhibit obsessive, uncontrolled patterns, such as grooming floors and carpets, pacing, rubbing fingers or hands, or clutching at clothes, try worry beads, baby toys, stuffed animals, or Nerf balls for them to manipulate. Learn to tolerate the pacing. Establish a safe and secure area for this activity. Although difficult to live with, it affords exercise and seems to vent energy that may arise from increasing anxiety about no longer being familiar with the surroundings, the house, family, or spouse. It also stimulates appetite and aids sleep.

Maintain as calm an environment as possible. One brave man walking this difficult path of deterioration describes noise and confusion as cause for his brain to shut down. He finds the best remedy is to sit quietly in a darkened room. Yet he encourages those with this affliction to continue trying to make progress. Smiles and laughter with those he meets are his challenge. Distraction by changing the subject or focus of attention is much better than arguing with your loved one. Dr. James C. Folsom, director of the International Center for the Disabled in New York City, told a story about an AD patient in the hospital who began to clamor, "There's a man under my chair!" The nurse repeatedly denied this but with no apparent comfort to the patient. Finally in desperation the nurse responded to the cry of the frightened patient by bending over and shouting "Boo!" under the patient's wheelchair. Then she announced, "There. He's gone."

Admonishing the nurse later, Dr. Folsom made it clear that one should not acknowledge a person's confusion or argue about the reality of it. It is much better to change the focus of attention to something more pleasing or nonthreatening. Glance out the window and ask the person's opinion about the possibility of rain. This is a simple but effective way to move out of a situation. It does nothing to aggravate either the victim or the caregiver. If the focus of hostility is aimed at you, leave the room briefly and reenter. It can be enough to disrupt the aggressive pattern of thought.

Intentionally keep the person in touch with reality. There are a number of ways to do this. Put a plastic-coated message board or chalkboard in a conspicuous place. Post on it the day, month, year, and other pertinent messages, such as where you are going, your time of return, and a phone number where you can be reached. If the person continues to repeat a question, write the answer on a file card. Have them carry it in a pocket so they can take it out and read it when needed. A reminder to read the card is easier than explaining again and again. For a long period of time this procedure was extremely comforting for Mother. Her heartfelt expressions of appreciation for this little gesture spoke volumes.

Using the same idea, post on the refrigerator door the day's schedule or any sequence of events the person has trouble remembering. Be quick to reward accomplishments with immediate praise. And, don't affirm confusions. Correct and reorient with frequent reminders of place, date, and time. Respond to confusion with facts whenever possible. This is a good general rule, except for those who burst into tears daily after the repeated inquiry about and news of a loved one's death. For them, it may be wiser to use evasion and distraction.

Be attentive to a balanced diet and regular exercise for both the afflicted and yourself. This is a tall order and one many people with no particular health problems fail to fulfill with discipline. Planning simple menus once or twice a week can save time and avoid that daily four o'clock hassle of "What's for dinner?" Dad had a two-week rotating menu he wrote out and repeated regularly, saving much time and energy in planning, shopping, and meal preparation. He loved preparing a dish for church potluck dinners, taking Mother, tasting someone else's cooking, and engaging in social conversation.

Establish a routine and stick to it as much as possible. Save time and temper by always placing such things as keys and glasses in the same location. Strive for consistency in the daily schedule and in your manner of response to the afflicted person. Keep these goals in mind: speak clearly, firmly state the business at hand, and anticipate understanding and compliance. For example, my father stopped asking Mother if she wanted to go for a walk. In their present routine he simply announces, "It's time for our walk. Let's get ready and go." My parents made this transition smoothly, as Mother was accustomed to complying with Dad's wishes throughout their married life. However, it can be very difficult for the caregiver who has not been a take-charge partner in the marriage or family.

In addition to becoming the primary decision maker, the caregiver must adapt to many other new roles. For example, a husband may now have to assume the role of meal planner, grocery shopper, cook, and housekeeper. Or a wife may now have to make decisions about financial planning, bookkeeping, household repairs, and car maintenance. Adapting to change comes hard. These changing roles grow slowly and must be nourished by considerable patience, courage, and determination. Disheartened caregivers who lack these qualities, or the will to develop them, can slowly slide into oppressive depression or even alcoholism. It is frustrating and heartbreaking, and it accelerates the decision about nursing home care.

My father established a daily 4:30 "libation" date with a widower friend. They agreed upon a limit of one drink before dinner. This has become routine and both have the opportunity for stimulating conversation, sharing family news, problems, and minor accomplishments. Dad fixes Mother a glass of milk with a bit of Kahlúa, and she participates in her simple way on the fringes of their conversation.

Encourage decision making and participation to the fullest extent possible in routine skills and meaningful activities. For the afflicted person, the level of participation in the garden club, Rotary, or church group will be affected. However, the benefits from continuing membership and attendance can bring a sense of fellowship and connection with others. This can be done only by openly informing associates about the problem. The presence of an afflicted one among a group can stimulate growth, compassion, and caring on the part of others.

# 5     LATER STAGES

AT THIS POINT it becomes difficult to separate usual family responses from helpful responses. Do whatever works for you and is also beneficial for the impaired person. As the disease progresses, one must allow more time for everything. This may mean giving up activities or getting some help.

Consider safety factors: post emergency numbers and your home address near every phone. You might try covering the stove top or sink faucets. Dad placed a pan upside down over the bathroom sink faucets after Mother, unable to figure out how to turn them off, stood helplessly watching the water run over the rim. She went looking for him outside only after water had soaked the carpet in the entire mobile home where they now live. He has since solved this problem by installing a large rubber washer under the sink plug, which keeps it from stopping up the drain.

A smoker with AD must be monitored and matches put away. By keeping cigarettes and ashtrays out of sight he or she may forget to ask about them. Smoke alarms should be checked regularly. Eliminate extension cords wherever possible, but provide plenty of lighting in every room and especially at stairs, where a good handrail ideally extends beyond the top and bottom steps. If advisable, place a baby gate at the top or bottom of the stairs. Power tools might need to be locked away, and certainly any guns or other weapons should be dismantled or removed.

Clearly labeled medications are best kept locked even if closed with child resistant caps. Alcoholic beverages also need to be inaccessible, as drinking can increase confusion—and it's easy to forget having just had one. Confusion is also exacerbated by clutter and noise. Keep the mail, magazines, and newspapers that clutter all our homes picked up and disposed of.

The mental processes necessary for chewing and swallowing are often affected, and choking can become a life-threatening reality. Using food processors or blenders can reduce this danger. Prepare hearty soups, stews, ground-meat casseroles, or any foods that become soft or spoon-manageable in cooking. You may have to put the spoon in the person's hand several times throughout the meal to get the pattern of eating started. If spills are a problem, try a baby plate with suction bottom. The point is to encourage independence as long as possible. Provide smaller meals and supplement them with healthful finger foods for snacks. Mother's weight has dropped significantly in recent months. She often wakes in a hostile mood demanding that Dad wake up. Part of this may be inexpressible hunger. The director of nursing for an AD unit in a large nursing home in Stamford, Connecticut, notes that the increased pacing in these later stages stimulates tremendous appetites. She provides peanut butter and jelly sandwiches for bedtime snacks.

Be prepared for behavior that is shocking to the uninformed. Accidental shoplifting is an innocent occurrence that could cause big problems. The Alzheimer's Association chapter in western North Carolina provides a business-size card with this simple statement: "My companion has a memory disorder. Please excuse any unusual behavior. Thanks for your patience." These would be useful in many instances, such as when dining in restaurants or when needing to enter public rest rooms together.

Rocks, hairbrushes, silverware, pencils, mail, dentures, jewelry, and eyeglasses can disappear in the trash, clog the toilet, become hidden in the refrigerator, or disrupt the laundry. Remove valuables and put them in a locked box or safety deposit box. It took us three years of periodic searching to find the family silver hidden in a lamp shade box in a cluttered corner of the attic. We knew then that we were battling an invisible, insidious enemy. The constant misplacing of things is in itself enough to drive entire families to distraction.

Lock doors if the person is prone to wander. If that does not suffice, install a high latch to solve the problem. A deadbolt lock is a sure solution, but this requires ready access to keys and can be an inconvenience. Many devices are available to use in situations where it is difficult to achieve security. I called the Alzheimer's Association at 800-272-3900 for information on security products. They immediately sent a five-page list of available products that included the manufacturing company, a description of the product, and often the cost. These devices may qualify for Medicaid reimbursement in some states.

A medical identification bracelet with name, address, phone number, and the message "memory impaired" is extremely important. Your local pharmacy can order these. They are also available through the Alzheimer's Association's Safe Return program. Nearly every AD family has its "wandering" stories to tell. One of the members of our support group related the first indication her family had that something was seriously wrong with her father. It happened on a late November day when they found him walking down the middle of the nearby turnpike without a coat. He had no idea where he was or where he lived.

At this stage you will want to investigate the kinds of social services available for in-home help along with initial inquiries into nursing home care (see chaps. 8 and 9). If legal matters have not been investigated carefully, then much has been lost in terms of future planning. These matters will need to be addressed urgently (see chap. 2). These investigations take an incredible amount of time. Simply visiting a nursing home to make inquiries is time consuming. Even imagining your loved one in such an institution is a difficult matter to comprehend and accept. A family member, trusted friend, doctor, lawyer, or minister can be of help. Ask for it.

Be conscientious about taking care of yourself as the caregiver. As the disease progresses, your time and energy become more consumed in caring for the other. Begin to plan for ways to adjust to the increasing demands. This may involve relocating to be nearer younger family members, entering a retirement complex that has health care facilities, simplifying your living to smaller, more easily manageable quarters, and/or hiring help to come into your home.

I interviewed a young New York City woman married to a man in his late fifties. Theirs was a rich and happy marriage, producing two beautiful children. Shortly after the second child was born, doctors diagnosed her husband with AD. This once-vibrant wife, now wearing that subdued and stricken look of so many caregivers, told me, "My good friends ask me the hard questions. 'Why are you still keeping him at home? When are you going put him in an institution?' I appreciate their challenging me with these questions. They force me to stop denying the reality of how bad it is and to begin thinking about options for the future. When Tom began being abusive to our son he's always adored, we moved him to our cottage with a hired caregiver. He's better there where life is simpler. I realized when we were together over the holidays that for him now, I'm simply another kind of presence. That realization [detachment] has helped me begin to address seriously the selection of a home for him."

Decisions about where to live are most difficult. Where is the best place for you to make this pilgrimage together? Perhaps the wisest choice is to stay where you are. But don't be too hasty in limiting your options. Entering into this decision process was probably the most difficult challenge our family encountered. My parents had carefully purchased their home with retirement years in mind. Now, for the first time in their fifty years of marriage, they could not make a major decision together about their future. Looking to other family members is helpful, but it can also be confusing. They each see the situation differently and propose solutions that coincide with their view of the problem. There is generally no one satisfactory solution.

One of the most helpful exercises my father worked out was to make a list of his options.

### OPTIONS TO EVALUATE

1. Maintain present home

   Advantages                 Disadvantages


2. Sell present home and rent apartment nearby

   Advantages                 Disadvantages


3. Sell present home, move residence to Florida mobile home park (site of several winter vacations) and rent summer home in Pennsylvania

   Advantages        Disadvantages


*Comments*
1. If I become incapacitated, "D" will need nursing home care.

2. If "D" becomes incapacitated and requires nursing home care, I need suitable quarters conveniently located near the home.
3. Where and how can I place the least future burden on others?
4. Where and how can I be of most help to others? (nebulous)

I would add to this list a vital factor we all overlooked: What support services are available in the location under consideration that would provide maximum help (see chap. 8).

After careful consideration, it became obvious that the second option was the wisest choice. However, in living with that idea for several months and looking unsuccessfully for a suitable apartment, another option began to grow and take shape. It was the ultimate choice.

It is a joy now to hear Dad speak contentedly about returning to their home in Florida. But the period of extreme turmoil and the pain of detachment were also very real when they decided to sell the Ohio house and distribute their belongings. It was a monumental undertaking that demanded the best efforts of the entire family (see "Simplifying," pp. 121–22 in the "Poems" section). I will write more about detachment later.

Dad and Mother now reside in a mobile home park in Florida. For several years they traveled north for visits with our family. They enjoyed the rural summer and early fall beauty of Maine with my sister and her family. Although this pattern of mobility is not ideal for the afflicted person, the anticipation of change and intimate family involvement served as a restorative for my father.

Dad's appreciation for the security and confines of the Florida mobile home park, equipped with an electronic security gate, became more pronounced after an autumn visit to Maine when the volunteer fire department and police had to help find Mother. She had wandered nearly five miles from my sister's home. She began to repeat these wanderings until finally the door closed for these annual weeks of reprieve for Dad. I will always fondly recall the pleasant autumn hikes we took together during their last visit to our home in Connecticut.

The park in Florida is small and the residents most kind. With great difficulty, Dad was finally able to share Mother's problem with them. They responded by discreetly keeping an eye out for her. Their home is a place the family enjoys visiting in winter. We space our visits so that someone is on the scene with some regularity.

The enormous decisions demanded by AD affect the remainder of your own life as well as the life of your loved one. In making and acting upon such major decisions, heavy demands fall on the shoulders of the caregiver. Remember that you are a person who needs friends, love, food, rest, and entertainment. You also have sexual and emotional needs.

# 6 SEXUAL AND EMOTIONAL NEEDS

An old friend I hadn't seen in months approached me at a recent social event. Ours was a warm greeting. As she lit a cigarette, I inquired about the state of things in her life. Tossing her wispy blonde curls, she blew a low chuckle of smoke toward the ceiling. "You know, my father has been getting awfully forgetful lately. Mother called the other day to tell me he can't remember the last time they had sex, so every day he's after her, trying to get her to go to bed." We laughed. She added, "Mom told me that the next time I'm out enjoying myself on the tennis court, I should remember where she is and what she's doing, and be grateful!"

In all my meetings with AD support groups, in studying, listening to lectures, and talking with people, seldom is the subject of sexual needs addressed.[1] I do not believe we should make the assumption that this is not a problem for many. Our sexuality is as much a part of our humanness and our personalities as are our capacity and need for good food, pleasant surroundings, and social intercourse with good friends. It is a gift of God.

Careful listening to joking complaints about "living like a monk for three years" can be translated into unspoken frustration. We must address this issue as Alzheimer's disease becomes diagnosed more and more among those in their forties, fifties, and sixties.

For the afflicted, forgetting where the bathroom is can bring about behavior that is shocking to the unprepared or unknowing public. Urinating into a bush, onto a public building, inside a store, onto an air vent in the living room, or defecating in a chair, has nothing to do with sexuality. But once sexual organs are exposed a new concern begins.

Public masturbation horrifies the most understanding caregiver. Yet such behavior simply confirms the continued sexual needs of the afflicted. Fondling the genitals feels good. If it is one's conviction that such behavior done in private is wrong, then accepting such a method of sexual release for either the afflicted person or the caregiver mate may be very difficult, but not impossible.[2]

A seventy-three-year-old man told a personal story that helps us understand the guilt many face because of legends we've grown up with. His mother made it clear to him as a child that everything one does is reflected into the sky, where God takes a picture. He certainly didn't want God taking a picture of him "doing that!" Many years later, a respected minister freed him from this crippling childhood myth by patiently explaining that a loving God judges human behavior according to the individual's intentions, and specific situations and circumstances. That we are known by such a loving and understanding God continues to be true when one's marriage partner is no longer able to participate in marital sexual relations.

For some, the mental impairment that changes a spouse results in a feeling of repulsion. For others, sexual needs have diminished and the onset of disease is a deciding factor in forgoing sexual relations altogether. Sexual relations with your afflicted spouse may be impossible. However, if your lifelong habits of marital sex have been expressed within the generosity of mutual love and caring, the desire to participate in the comfort of shared intimacy may continue. Meaningful and satisfying expressions of marital love are possible even into the advanced stages of the disease. For both partners, the sexual experience can serve as a distraction from the cycle of sadness. It remains a valid and healthy way of releasing energy. It is a therapeutic interlude, a normal expression between two loving people.

We learned earlier about the importance of physical touch and the craving for affection many victims of AD, stroke, Parkinson's, and other mentally disruptive diseases exhibit. Make use of this desire to help satisfy your own sexual needs as well. One woman whose husband is now operating at the level of a two-year-old told me, "We spend a lot of time in the evenings just cuddling on the couch. It gives us both comfort."

Aggressive, demanding, sexually frustrated advances will probably frighten the afflicted partner into a panic or even violent behavior. "Get out of here. You're not my husband!" This may happen in spite of a gentle, loving approach. Try again another time.

One man in his mid-seventies told me that his wife, in the advanced stages of AD, had forgotten who he was. He confided with a mixed degree of embarrassment and pride that, after engaging in sex recently with her, she seemed more attentive to him. She referred to him lovingly as "my husband" throughout the next day or so.

In sexual matters, as in many others, distraction serves well to alter unacceptable behavior in inappropriate times and places. Humor, as we shall see in chapter 11, can break the spell of a brewing battle of wills.

If an AD caregiver came to you for advice on how to remain emotionally stable given the reality of all the unrelenting demands caregivers face, what would you say? The director of a municipal department on aging responded to that question this way: "Take care of yourself. Don't neglect your own needs. Plan ahead and don't allow yourself to become an emotionally and physically exhausted prisoner."

"How does one avoid that?" I asked.

She replied, "We are accustomed to a lifetime of attention to our physical needs; what they are and how to meet them. We are less accustomed to evaluating our emotional needs. Yet the ability to define and fulfill them can help keep us from becoming such a prisoner."

I said, "But some scoff and say, 'I don't have time; besides, I don't know how to define and fulfill my emotional needs.'"

To this observation, she replied thoughtfully, "That's a common response. Sometimes caring and just *being there* are more important than *doing* for the other. There's a difference between complaining that gets problem solving started, and complaints that simply reinforce negative feelings. Caregivers don't have much time to think about their needs, but if freedom and emotionally fulfilled living are important, it's worth the effort. Each evening try to recall with gratitude at least one good thing that happened during the day. Caregivers probably will need to learn some different methods of expressing anger in healthy and acceptable ways. I encourage them to use available support systems: family, friends, doctor, clergy and church, support groups, counselors, therapists, and community resources. Get a buddy system going with another caregiver. There is no magic that can help change our loved one; we can only change how we relate to them, and maintaining a sense of personal freedom and emotional fulfillment makes for better care-givers."

The burden of care usually falls on the spouse and/or one adult child with intense (and often unspoken) resentment of the others who are not as involved. Feelings of despair and anger are common. "Why me?" is the eternal cry of pain that haunts both victim and family stricken by such a devastating life tragedy. Unless one can surmount the temptation to remain in the unhappy place of looking for the answer to that unanswerable question, the caregiver may become less and less able and willing to make major decisions and seek assistance. Fatigue and poor diet can bring about a frustrated surrender to unreasonable behavior. The question that needs to be posed is, What can I (we) do to best manage the problems we face? This makes it clear that communication among family members and close friends is important, and other support systems vital.

We have said nothing about the guilt feelings that can depress the afflicted person.[3] Unable to understand fully and remember why the spouse or adult child is assuming more and more responsibility, most seem to experience some mixed guilt and anger, particularly in the earlier stages. This may be expressed in outbursts of rage. Their territory (of responsibility) is being invaded and they can't remember why. For many, periods of severe depression and withdrawal serve to protect them. They, too, need the help of those listed above to maintain the ties that bind them emotionally to the rest of humanity.

There is a heightened sense of sadness in bidding farewell to a loved one who now barely resembles the person of the past. Incredibly hard emotional work needs to be done. A lifetime of being self-sufficient and working through problems, particularly emotional problems, either alone or within the limits of the family makes the outward turning for help and support an extremely difficult stance for many. Be encouraged. One learns humility in asking for help. Your reaching out provides growth for you as well as for the ones who respond. We all are beneficiaries.

# 7     ADVANCED STAGES

THE ADVANCED STAGES of this disease march unrelentingly along—sometimes rapidly, sometimes with barely perceptible change. In addition to memory impairment we find visual perception, speaking, eating, reading, writing, and walking affected. And, hallucinations may occur. The caregiver suffers a total lack of privacy, being followed everywhere by the afflicted, even into the bathroom. For several years, Mother was uneasy when Dad was anywhere out of her sight. Now the search for "home" seems to occupy her much of the time. When we ask "What home?" she cannot express the focus of her longing, since there apparently is no longer a home she can recognize either in reality or in her memory.

Pacing, screaming, erratic sleep patterns, and night wandering are common. These disturbing behaviors often become more severe during certain daily routines such as bathing, or in the evening, a condition referred to by professionals as *sundowning*. Using their own bedroom furniture, we fixed a room for my parents in our home, hoping they would feel more comfortable with us. However, Mother interrupted our sleep as she roamed from room to room, getting in bed with us in her confusion. It was apparent she was often much calmer and more alert upon waking in the morning. We came to appreciate how the primary caregiver suffers from the draining weariness. Because of the confined space of their mobile home and the nature of Mother's wanderings, silent and without apparent fear, this is not a major problem. For many, though, it becomes a waking nightmare. But, assuring the confused person that she is where she is supposed to be, that she is safe and you are there with her, often gets her back to sleep. This kind of diplomacy isn't easy in the dark cold hours of night.

We leave the bathroom light on and use night-lights in the hall and bedroom to provide a path of light. A glass of milk or substantial snack just before bedtime is also helpful. Family pictures in the bedroom help the person feel at home and may even prevent the wandering in search of "home."

Dad has discovered that Mother's sleep patterns respond amazingly to regular exercise. For four years their routine included morning exercises upon arising, a vigorous twenty-minute walk before breakfast, a short nap in the early afternoon, then a swim, and a walk before dinner or just before bed. Now Mother refuses to participate in morning exercises. She accompanies Dad on their walks, sometimes with pleasure, other times grudgingly. She no longer naps and is now afraid of both swimming and boating.

An Alzheimer's Association newsletter speaks to the problems of medication and wandering. It warns: "Use restraints with great caution. Many injuries result in older persons from improperly applied restraints." Drugs have a definite place in the management of the night-wandering or aggressively agitated person.[1]

"The choice of drug and the dosage must be tailor-made for each individual. Several factors must be taken into account: age, general physical condition, other medications, and the degree of agitation or wandering. Older people do not metabolize drugs as quickly as do younger ones so the drug will remain longer in the older person's system. Use sedation with caution and only as prescribed by a physician."[2] A safe motto might be "start low and go slow." On the other hand, giving a drug only when the person seems to need it can be unsuccessful, since many medications must be administered regularly over a period of time so that the blood level achieves and maintains the necessary dosage to be helpful.

Researchers and pharmaceuticals are scrambling to discover, test, and get to market inexpensive and reliable ways to diagnose AD, and drugs to postpone the onset of AD or alleviate early symptoms. They are also working on behavioral and drug treatments that are effective for those further along in the disease process. To date, the drug Aricept is the only drug social workers and professional health care workers I've interviewed are talking about. It seems to be the best at improving cognitive skills for some people. Surely more choices of effective drug therapies will come along soon.

Here are some behavioral skills you might try. Continue to speak clearly and directly to the afflicted one. State who you are, why you're there, and what you're doing to help. Give directions calmly as if you expect compliance. "Techniques that have been successful in small studies of getting dressed include having the caregiver demonstrate what to do, so the patient can mimic the action. Another technique is laying out clothes in the order that they should be put on... or prompting with simple statements, [one step at a time] like, 'Pick up the shirt. Put your arm in the sleeve,' perhaps using touch to show which arm. Improved functioning seems to go along with a significant improvement in the behavioral problems."[3]

Remove inappropriate clothing from the closet. Choose clothes that are simple to put on and launder. Dad was grateful for the discovery of thigh-high stockings (available through Sears or Penney catalogs). Dressing up became much easier for both of them.

Pockets for reminder cards are helpful. When possible, forgo difficult underwear such as bras. Use soft undershirts or camisoles and half-slips. Soft knit slacks for men and women are available that just pull on. Do anything to simplify your job. Learn to divert the person's attention to other things to avoid hostilities. Remember the power of gentle touch and praise. When possible, do things *with*, not to, the afflicted. Though this approach eventually becomes unrealistic, "We're in this together" is a powerful message to convey to your loved one. This attitude can guide your holy task of giving care, yet the patience it requires is not always possible.

Try not to be overprotective. Nothing angers my father more than having someone hold Mother's hand while they are out for their walk. "Don't *baby* her!" is his cry. He is fiercely determined that she do all she can for herself if it is humanly possible. This means that he walks her step by step through every act of bathing, eating, toileting, getting dressed and undressed, hanging up clothes, putting away shoes, brushing teeth, and exercising. Although stretched frequently to the limits of utter frustration, my father has the patience of a saint, which he never did before. It has been a slow, painful evolution.

As the litany of loss continues, the disease begins to affect bladder and bowel control, and it causes loss of speech and confinement to bed.

Death often occurs when infection invades the body and brings on pneumonia. Each person walks this grim path in his or her unique way, suffering gradual mental and physical deterioration without a specific, predictable progression.

No family responds in the same way to these unwanted days. By this time, financial resources ought to have been analyzed carefully and all legal powers of attorney established. Comparisons between nursing home care, in-home care, or day care should have been made (see chap. 8). Most family members who have worked together to assist the primary caregiver up to this point will continue to serve as tremendous support in these later stages.

Adult children geographically removed and busy with their own lives often avoid responsibility and experience guilt. I encourage them to maintain helpful involvement in the following ways: Space visits so that someone is on the scene at fairly regular intervals. Phone regularly at different times of the day and week to see how things are going. Get acquainted with neighbors and supportive friends of your parents. When visiting, do the legwork and make necessary phone inquiries to track down whatever available in-home assistance is needed. Regularly write or e-mail the parent caregiver. Listen carefully for masked or outright cries for help. For the sake of your own generation, get actively involved in creating political pressure to change laws that discriminate against AD families in a cruel, inhuman way, and to fund research into the cause and prevention of this dreadful disease. As AD has been estimated to cost the nation $80 to $90 billion a year, it is in your own best interest to do so.[4] After age sixty-five, the percentage of affected people approximately doubles with every decade of life.

## PERSONAL HYGIENE

In an essay that Stanley M. Aronson, M.D., wrote about AD sufferers in Rhode Island, statistics are staggering: "Current studies identify close to 4,500 AD patients confined to the nursing homes of Rhode Island. Another eight hundred are virtually permanent residents of the various state and federal hospitals of this region and yet another five to eight thousand are estimated to be still living in their homes. In excess of one in every one hundred Rhode Islanders is now afflicted with AD."[5] Though the population of Rhode Island is admittedly more elderly than most states, these statistics, translated broadly across the world population, suggest a critical need for information and coping skills in the difficult area of personal hygiene, particularly for caregivers in the home.[6]

Encourage involvement in personal hygiene as long as possible. In this most exasperating and demanding aspect of responsibility the title "caregiver" is earned. Try as much as possible to explain in a calm, quiet manner what you need to do. The afflicted person quickly picks up your distress or disgust and this can be extremely upsetting. If necessary, walk away from the task until you can come back to it more calmly. Besides providing a clean body, your attitude can also minister to the other in immeasurable ways.

Personal hygiene, particularly for the male caregiver, is one of the most difficult areas to manage. As the disease progresses, toileting habits of wiping and flushing are lost. A growing fear of water often adds complications. This means constant experimentation with various approaches. People have shared with me some of the following creative methods:

"We give ourselves sponge baths at the kitchen sink. As I wash myself, I tell her what to do and she washes herself."

"I put a sturdy Styrofoam cooler (weighted down) in the tub for him to sit on. Then I wash him down. A rubber shower hose attached to the faucet helps."

"We have a molded vinyl chair for the tub. Small squares of thin rubber rug padding under each leg make it secure. The back helps her know which way to face and gives her something to hold onto when getting into the tub. We installed a handheld shower attachment."

"I put some water in the tub and help her get in. While I shave, I tell her what to do to wash. When I'm done, she's ready to get out."

"I always have him look in the mirror when I shave him. Otherwise, he is afraid."

"We've decided it's easier to let his beard grow and keep it clipped."

"We have a large stall shower. It's easiest for me when we shower together."

Modesty for some is a serious inhibitor to good personal hygiene. Unless help is hired, one must move beyond the embarrassment and begin to see it as a job that needs doing in a matter-of-fact manner.

## INCONTINENCE

A member of our support group did a meticulous study of forty-four AD patients. It showed that incontinence is not necessarily a symptom only of very advanced stages of AD. It can occur even in the early stages.[7] However, it does often seem to be the final blow for the caregiver who is trying to maintain the afflicted person at home. No matter how many helpful tips one might get or how many aids that help manage the problem, this loss of control makes most caregivers begin the search in earnest for a nursing home.

For those approaching this stage or already grappling with this humbling form of servitude, some help is available.[8] If your loved one is in bed a great deal, keeping the skin clean and dry is of utmost importance. Bedsores are caused by pressure and made worse by moisture. Prevent this by moving the person every two hours by raising the foot of the bed or changing position with pillows. Try using water mattresses, egg-crate foam, or air pads and/or mattresses. Keep the bottom sheet wrinkle free, clean, and free of crumbs. Gently massage the skin with lotion to help circulation.

Getting the person to the bathroom every two to three hours can help alleviate incontinence problems for some time. Try not to be abusive or sarcastic; rather, aim for a positive attitude with a phrase such as, "Let's work on this problem together." Cut back on fluids in the evening. Catheterization may be a simple though dramatic solution to this problem that will allow home care much longer. Members of our support group agree that the use of large-size Pampers or similar disposable diapers for a smaller adult often work as well as more costly brands for adults. The savings are considerable; try different brands.

Disposable pads for bed and chairs are available, but they are more expensive than waterproof sheets. A three-foot square is adequate protection and washable cotton-backed rubber pads are most comfortable. Protect the mattress either with a plastic mattress cover or an opened garbage bag used as a draw sheet under the mattress pad. If an accident occurs and the bed must be changed, involve the afflicted person in helping to change the sheets.

For bowel incontinence, the emphasis once again is on prompt cleaning and drying of the skin. There are products that aid in eliminating odors and cleansing the skin, making the job less offensive. Wearing rubber gloves or using disposable gloves can also help reduce the unpleasantness of the task.

Some caregivers coping with this problem produced these suggestions:

"I call myself by another name when I'm bathing or changing him. That seems to make him more at ease."

"When I'm changing her diaper, we keep a scarf by the bed and I tell her to cover her eyes. If she can't see me doing the work, she's calmer about it."

One home health care aide who cared for a friend until she died said, "We make a game of it. When I want to bathe her, she clamps her knees together. So I say, 'Come on, Jeanie, it's time to open up the safe.' She then relaxes and I can wash her properly."

One woman whose husband repeatedly removes the disposable diapers she puts on him at bedtime has discovered that layering newspapers under him in the night helps keep him warm and dry.

"It's easier on both of us to have him lie down on the bed to change him. I'm careful about his diet, so his stools are just soft. If he's really a mess or if the stool is hard and dried, I put him on the portable sitz bath that fits on the toilet [these are available at pharmacies where products for disabled persons are sold]. The warm water with a little liquid soap in it feels good to him. Bounty paper towels are good for cleaning and drying."

"I keep her fingernails cut quite short. Sometimes she gets her hands inside her diaper before I know she needs changing and she smears it all over."

"Lotions are available to help keep the skin dry, but I use the same things I used on our babies to prevent diaper rash: zinc oxide ointment or Desitin. These are a little messier but cheaper."

Hospital nurses, nurse gerontologists, and nursing home staff all recommend patient and persistent efforts to achieve bowel management. They make it their primary objective.

Constipation, a common problem, can be helped or even eliminated by attention to a bowel-training program. It is important to know the lifelong bowel habits of the person. For some, a normal pattern is a bowel movement only once in two or three days. Increased restlessness, searching about, often precedes the need to empty bowels. Being alert to this behavior and leading the person to the toilet can help prevent accidents.

The following are ways to encourage normal bowel habits:
1. Mild exercise: as much physical activity as the person can safely tolerate.
2. Bulk and fluids in the diet: natural foods such as fruits, vegetables, bran cereal, and two quarts of liquids daily. Plenty of water.
3. Laxatives: Natural are preferred (prunes, figs, sauerkraut). Either hot liquids or ice water immediately after breakfast can stimulate contractions of the lower intestine. Try a cup of Super Dieter's Tea before bedtime. If they work for you, these natural laxatives are preferred to stool softeners.[9] If not, Colace is a frequently used stool softener that adds bulk and acts as a stimulant to the lower bowel, though generic brands work well and are less expensive. Your physician or pharmacist can make other recommendations.
4. Enemas: Your physician can prescribe the type, frequency, and amount to be used. Cleaning the lower bowel with a Fleet enema is a good way to begin a bowel-management program. If stool is hard and the person has difficulty evacuating, filling an empty Fleet bottle with warm water and using it as an enema can help. Laxatives and enemas are not part of an ongoing bowel-management program, but they aid in establishing such a regimen.

5.  Regularity: Establish a routine time for evacuation. This can begin
    with a nightly glass of prune juice or an ounce of bran eaten with
    breakfast. Prior to breakfast (or other meal, if preferable), use a glyc-
    erin suppository. If that is not effective, insert a Dulcolax supposi-
    tory about one and a half inches into the rectum. (Dulcolax
    suppositories are available over the counter. One word of caution:
    they can cause cramping.) A bowel movement will usually result in
    twenty to forty minutes. This is done with least resistance if the per-
    son lies on her or his side facing away from you, with the top knee
    pulled up toward the chin. Hemorrhoids are common in the elderly
    and can be extremely painful. One nurse I interviewed suggested
    that after bowel movements or when inserting suppositories, sim-
    ply push protruding hemorrhoids up above the internal sphincter
    of the rectum to bring enormous relief. After eating, get the person
    to the toilet, allowing fifteen to thirty minutes for the effort of
    achieving a bowel movement. Toileting terms used in childhood
    will often convey the message better. Elevating the feet with the
    knees above the hips on a small stool in front of the toilet often
    helps evacuate the bowel.

This regimen requires a willingness to experiment with a combination
of suggestions that work best for your afflicted one. It can be tailored as
you progress. With careful attention to diet and fluids, the routine use
of suppositories and stool softeners may be gradually discontinued after
a successful bowel-management program is well in place. This can take
six to eight weeks. Once established, however, any interruption in this
daily routine may jeopardize the progress you have made.

Try to change your focus from the lost capabilities to those simple
things the person can do, remembering the power of praise. Do not reward unsatisfactory behavior. Often a frown or shake of the head is
enough to change a pattern of response. One of our group members remarked, "Sometimes I have to give her my hard voice and that usually
gets things back on track. She knows I mean business."

All these things are difficult to manage consistently. One simply
must have an escape from it regularly. Extending yourself on the other's
behalf, maintaining his or her dignity as much as possible, is a daily
demonstration of committed love. But there are limits. A conversation
with a robust Chicago man whose wife just four years ago served as ex-

ecutive secretary to the president of one of the largest corporations in the United States proves the point: "Now that she's incontinent things are really going downhill. I can't make her lie down or bend over so I can get her cleaned. She just stands there all messed up, rigid and staring at me. Thank God someone told me about this spray stuff to use to get rid of the odor while you're cleaning them up. Lately I've been smacking her to try to get her to snap out of it and do what I tell her...sometimes harder than I mean to. But it's so damned frustrating!"[10]

How rare to find one so honest. This story illustrates merely the tip of the iceberg of abuse of the elderly and severely handicapped by worn-out and frustrated caregivers both in the home and in institutions.[11] When you find yourself screaming often or feeling the temptation to strike the afflicted, it's time to get help. Anything that will make your life easier will also improve the quality of life for your loved one. This may mean care from others in an institution.

# 8

D∪E TO INCREASING awareness of the cost of institutionalizing those needing custodial care, legislators are beginning to support bills funding a developing network of services for older adults. Because of the growing complexity of this network, it is important to be clear about your needs when exploring available services.

Assessing needs is often hard for the primary caregiver. In her exceptional book *Home Health Care, A Complete Guide for Patients and Their Families,* Jo-Ann Friedman helps clarify confused ideas about the role of various aspects of the home health care team, making it easier to determine the kind of help one needs to seek. To obtain services requires patience and persistence in phoning and/or visiting agencies.[1] This is a task that takes enormous emotional and physical energy. If you as caregiver cannot muster what it takes, ask for help from an adult child or a younger friend you trust. Most private health care agencies have brochures describing their services. They will send these to you or come to your home to make arrangements for services. However, even these private agencies are not always the solution.

When my father became ill in the winter of 1985, it was evident immediately that a support system would be crucial. I made several contacts in Florida on behalf of my parents. First I called the minister. He was new to the church and unaware of Mother's condition, even though my parents are faithful in their regular attendance at worship. He seemed grateful for the information and asked what the church could do for them. I gave him concrete suggestions (see chap. 4), which included asking a few people to watch for them on Sundays. In their absence, I said, we would appreciate a phone call or visit to check on them. He handed me his card and said, "Tell Charles he should call me any time day or night when he needs help." I'm sure he meant it as a generous gesture, but emergency help is not the issue, and for my father to ask a busy minister for help is most unlikely.

Soon after my return home (with Dad back on his feet) the minister visited my parents. He gave Dad a list of names and numbers of people in the church who wanted to be their "guardians." Some time later, a group of young people doing clown ministry came to laugh with and entertain them. The call to the minister was a crucial first step in asking for help.

Next I called the doctor's office. He asked, "Is this a medical situation you wish to see me about?" I answered, "No, I simply would like to meet you and talk for a few minutes about ways I can get some help for my parents." The doctor told me, "I'm going to give you the name of the social worker at the hospital. Call her with your questions, and if you still wish to see me, call me back."

I was disappointed not to meet with him but grateful for the contact. I made an appointment with the hospital social worker. She impressed me by her sincere desire to be helpful. Overworked and understaffed, she sighed heavily. "I wish I could you tell you something that could give you hope for help. There is so little; no adult day-care program, no support group I know about. In fact, there is nothing we can do here. Have you been to the social services agency? Do you know about the hot lunch program at the senior center?" She gave me names and numbers to call. I walked to the nearby senior center, introduced myself, and met the director of the hot lunch program. We talked about my parents' situation.

"We've had to drop some people from the program because of a cut in funding," she said with despair. "But this is clearly a case of need. Your father must have some relief." She told me the cost per meal and added that most who come donate a dollar. I suggested it would help if my parents could come just twice a week. Dad would be willing to pay the full cost. "Then I think we can take them. I'll check with my supervisor and call you in the morning," she said.

The next day I made an appointment with the county social services agency, whose director of homemaker services had agreed Dad needed help. "I will come out to meet them and do an intake on Friday. We may only be able to get someone there twice a week for a couple of hours each time, but it's a start. Our purpose is to help keep people in their homes as long as possible. These services are free, but we request a donation."

Some of these agencies offer a handyman service for simple yard work, outdoor chores, and minor repairs. They, too, have difficulty finding people to work and obtaining the funds necessary to pay. We were told that if Dad became ill again, respite service would be available for taking temporary care of them until he recovered or until we could make other arrangements.

I was impressed by everyone's expressions of concern and desire to help, but I was discouraged by the lack of operating support systems and the dire financial straits of the few in operation. As of 1998, this condition has not changed much in that area. Local adult day care or an AD support group is still unavailable. Home health nurses are fretting about federal edicts coming down warning of caps "in the near future" on Medicare/Medicaid allowances for services. The agencies don't know if the services they are providing are going to be paid for. One home health nurse I spoke with told of the terrible plight of the impoverished trying to tough it out at home. "Some of our patients admit they are only taking one pill a day, when they should be taking three or four, because they can't afford the medication. We beg medicines for them from doctor's offices, pharmaceutical companies, anyone we think we can get them from. It's pitiful."

After hearing from the hot lunch director, I took my parents to the senior center to meet the director and look the place over. In his typically humorous manner, Dad quipped as we approached the door, "Should I turn down my hearing aid and limp badly?" This was his way of expressing discomfort at what we were doing.

It does take courage to walk through all those doors. Be encouraged. Be willing to accept help. Understand the need to reveal your monthly income to government agencies. Don't feel guilty for making use of their services. You've been paying taxes nearly a lifetime and can rejoice when such support is available to you.

Within a week after their first meal at the senior center, Dad reported glowingly of the good and generous portions. With a lift in his voice he also said that they went early enough for him to play bridge before lunch. Mother is one of several there with AD. People understand and are comfortable in accepting her limitations.

Before the director of the social services agency and her assistant came to meet my parents, I wrote the following letter for Dad to give to anyone who might come to take care of Mother. I showed it to the director. Later, she asked Dad for a copy to keep in her office file.

February 2, 1985
Dear Homemaker-helper-friend,

We very much appreciate your coming to help my parents. Mother will probably wonder for quite a while who you are and why you are here. Just tell her your name and that you are Martha and Charles's friend. She is happiest when she feels she is helping with things that need doing. She can dry dishes for you, but you will need to put them away. It will be important that you learn where Charles keeps things so he will be able to find them later. Dorothy can "help" you do other things: make the bed, change sheets, put things on the table for meals, do laundry, run sweeper or give her a dust cloth while you vacuum or sweep the porch. You'll soon discover other things you can do together. Mother is generally sweet tempered and so you will find her easy to be with. Keep aware of her bathroom needs. Dad likes for her to look nice and is wonderful about her personal care. When you talk with Charles, be sure to speak clearly and not too fast. He does quite well with his hearing aid.

Our whole family has tried hard to continue treating Mother as a grown person with a problem, not as a child. I know you will enjoy getting to know them both and help in their care. My brother in Chicago, my sister in Maine, my sister in Boston, and I will be forever grateful for what you can do to keep them together here in their home as long as possible.

Thank you and God bless you.

A young woman from the Homemaker Service began coming twice a week for two hours to keep track of Mother and to do some light housekeeping and the laundry. She offered to bathe Mother, shampoo her hair, and dress her if requested. Her services soon fell into a pattern of whizzing through the housekeeping chores as quickly as possible and then leaving. Perhaps because Dad chose not to involve her in Mother's personal care, companionship with and responsibility for Mother did not evolve. This arrangement lasted for five months. Funding was again cut and she was let go.

The agency then apologetically sent out a woman seventy-three years old whose physical frailty limited her ability to do much more than be a sitter for Mother. She visited once a month.

Later we found a young neighbor woman who had worked with retarded children. We hired her to come two afternoons a week. The entire family rejoiced in this arrangement, but it lasted only two weeks. She left reluctantly for a full-time job. (A year later, our hope for someone patient enough to include Mother in some simple tasks apparently remains too idealistic. We haven't yet accomplished this.)

We then turned to private home health agencies, with gratitude that such health care services are becoming more available. The cost keeps most caregivers from using these services until they have no other choice. In the Florida Keys area where my parents lived, the cost in 1998 was ten to fifteen dollars an hour for up to four hours of home health aide and one hundred dollars a day for twenty-four-hour live-in help. In North Carolina, where I now live, services for home health aide run about thirteen dollars an hour. Round-the-clock in-home care from a bonded caregiver can run up to one hundred thousand dollars a year. In Connecticut, hourly costs were quoted as thirteen dollars for a companion, fourteen for a personal care attendant, and eighteen for home health aide care.

Dad inquired at the only private health care agency in their area. The agency welcomed his call and sent someone to get the necessary information before beginning homemaker/companion services. The woman who arrived to work was pleasant enough. After about thirty minutes of housekeeping she took Mother for a walk in the park. Very shortly she returned alone, breathless and extremely upset. Mother had broken away from her. "She's running away... I can't possibly catch up with her... my back . . ." Dad soothed her, telling her to sit on the patio while he got on his bike to bring Mother back. When they returned, the woman stood and stated rather abruptly, "I am an RN. This is not the kind of work I had in mind." She left. The director of the agency apologized and said she was sorry she had no one else to send.

This series of events points to the need to explore the support services in an area before moving there. Though they are sadly lacking in the area where my parents live, progress is being made nationwide. Today one can call the Elder Care Locator at 800-677-1116 for information anywhere in the United States for local experts and resources. Your local Department on Aging will probably have a directory of services for seniors in your area.

Make phone calls to nearby agencies to ask questions about the range and cost of their services. Policies, services, and financing differ sometimes radically between agencies; for example, how the agency screens and trains employees, whether it requires a minimum number of hours per visit, whether it charges a placement fee. Be clear about the differences in services provided and cost, particularly the difference in the two categories of caregiver: homemaker/companion and home health aide.

You will get an immediate feel about the agency by the way its personnel treat you and respond to your questions. Conversations with four agency heads made it clear that the phrase "hands-on care" distinctly differentiates services offered by a home health aide and those by a homemaker/companion. If the patient needs any kind of washing (after using the toilet, for example) only home health aides are trained and permitted to give that kind of care in most instances. In addition, they will do light housekeeping, shopping, cooking, laundry, and offer companionship to the afflicted person. Aides also usually report to a nursing supervisor.

It can be an interesting quest to explore what is available to you. Be a good consumer. You are paying full fare. The cost for this custodial care is not covered by entitlements. However, in some states, like Connecticut, financial assistance for in-home care is available for some through the CT Home Health Fund for Elders program financed by Medicaid. Severe limitations on income and assets are required. Likewise, private long-term care insurance is available for those who can afford it and plan for it early enough.

## LONG-TERM CARE INSURANCE

A word on long-term care insurance (LTCI) for those trying to plan ahead: the United Seniors Health Cooperative, at 1331 H Street, N.W. Suite 500, Washington, DC 20005-4706 (phone 202-393-6222), publishes *Long-Term Care Planning: A Dollar and Sense Guide.* This provides a wealth of information on the subject. Their *Special Report # 34* on long-term care insurance answers the question of to buy or not to buy.[2] One must first understand that policies that have enough home care coverage to keep loved ones at home without family caregivers are not available. Family caregivers along with LTCI may make it possible for the afflicted person to remain at home longer. Generally, most LTCI policies don't pay back nearly as much as other types of health insurance, though insurance companies are improving available policies. They advise that one should avoid policies that pay only for "medically necessary" care. Look for a policy that covers cognitive as well as physical disabilities, paying benefits if you meet either criteria. As you get older, LTCI premium costs increase. If you plan to purchase LTCI, don't wait until a serious medical condition develops. You probably will be refused coverage.[3] The October 1997 issue of *Consumer Reports* magazine rates 114 long-term care insurance policies, helps you evaluate the need for the policies, outlines pitfalls to avoid, and suggests ways to judge various policies. A copy of this report is available from CU/Reprints, 101 Truman Ave., Yonkers, New York 10703-1057.

Tax laws in this area of long-term care have changed at least seven times since the first edition of this book ten years ago. Recent changes in the law concerning the medical expense deduction for LTCI makes "Taxes and Alzheimer's Disease: The Itemized Deduction for Medical Expenses," a brochure available from the Alzheimer's Association, most helpful. It gives general information and guidelines to assist you and your tax preparer in filing your return. Call your local chapter or 800-272-3900 to receive a copy.

Generally speaking, "under the long-term care provisions added to the Internal Revenue Code in 1996, certain payments received on account of a chronically ill individual from a qualified long-term care insurance contract are excluded from income."[4] To be qualified for this exclusion, the policy must include a "non-forfeiture" option (at additional cost), which protects the policyholder against losing the accrued value of the policy for a lapse in payments of premiums. As far as other tax deductions, check with your tax preparer about the deductibility of expenditures incurred for long-term care services, including unreimbursed expenses for goods and services that assist with activities of daily living or protection from threats to health and safety due to severe memory loss. This might include such items as dental care, glasses, hearing aids, prescription drugs, LTCI premiums, Medicare copayments, and deductibles. Cost for in-home care help, adult day care, or a residential care facility might also be deductible.[5] Laws affecting the elderly will probably be in a state of rapid change for years to come, making it wise to consult with someone well versed in these tax law matters.

## DAY CARE

Adult day-care centers are emerging in towns and cities across the nation, though they are not yet available in the Florida area where my parents live. The same careful investigation, visitation, and questioning must be done in locating a satisfactory day-care facility as is required in deciding upon a nursing home (see chap. 9).

There is natural resistance to investigating and participating in such a program. Fear of many things prevents us from action: quality of care, cost (twenty to sixty dollars per day with a sliding scale based on income, and in some an additional small charge for meals and transportation), disturbed behavior on the part of our loved one or others who attend, and admitting to ourselves that we can no longer handle the problem without help.

The experience of many, however, shows that when one is fortunate enough to have access to a day-care facility, the afflicted person is quickly distracted from the trauma of separation and soon becomes engaged in a variety of activities and conversations far more stimulating than those the primary caregiver can provide at home alone. The mutual work of detachment, for both afflicted and caregiver, can be nurtured by attending such day-care programs. The later dividends can be considerable.

It's a mistake to visit a center and judge what we see by our own standards of need rather than by those of the afflicted person. I have visited bright, spacious, and extremely attractive day-care facilities. I have also visited some that are drab and unappealing. Coming home from such a visit with a neighbor, we agreed we would never put our husbands in such a place with its dreary, old, temporary quarters.

We were unable at that time to assess the quality of interaction among people and the careful, thoughtful programming to help each person become involved to the best of his or her ability. A woman who had been attending this center under protest poignantly expressed this.

She repeatedly had accused her family of trying to put her away. After two weeks, however, she told her daughter as they were driving home, "I don't remember where I was but thank you for taking me there." Creatively industrious and caring personnel working toward the best program for each individual is what good day-care centers have in common.

Invite a staff person from a day-care center to speak to your group. You'll be amazed at the interesting variety of activities they offer and the effort they expend to tailor activities to meet individual needs. Such services by caring people surely postpone that day none of us look forward to: placing a loved one in a nursing home. However, we must prepare for that, too.

# 9   CHOOSING A NURSING HOME

PREMATURE PLACEMENT in a nursing home is certainly to be avoided. Ultimately, however, the realization dawns, "I can't hack it any more. If I go under, we both go." Then we must make a decision.

We are now talking about the need for twenty-four-hour care. To help avoid continually revisiting the decision, consider these questions: Have you the space and accommodations to support total in-home care? Have you exhausted the resources of services available to you in the home, whether privately paid or government subsidized? Have you analyzed the cost of in-home care? Does it exceed or come close to what nursing home care would cost? (This figure must include lost wages for working-age caregivers.) Is your own health suffering? For most people, a "no" to the first question and a "yes" to the last three should help in making a decision.

Other questions you might consider: Does my loved one know where he or she is? Would a change of environment make a difference? Am I personally recognized and being responded to or are the responses directed to the care given? Can I provide a safe environment at all times? Is the afflicted so physically strong that unintentional harm may come to me or other persons giving care? Would the varieties of socialization and therapy (music, occupational, physical) offered in a good nursing home benefit the afflicted?[1] Some of these are questions difficult to assess and answer objectively. Even within families, answers will differ.

You need to know what level of care your loved one needs and what levels of care are offered in the facilities you investigate. The lowest level of care is offered in rest homes, or assisted-living homes, where meals, some help with personal care, limited supervision, and occasional medical care are provided. Special assistance pays for these services only for the very poor. Intermediate care facilities (ICF) are for those who need more medical and personal assistance but who are still able to manage quite well in a protected setting. An RN is on duty eight hours, usually during the day. Medicaid pays for intermediate or skilled care, under specific income and resource tests. A skilled nursing care facility (SNF) is for those who cannot care for themselves and need professional health and medical care at all times, with one or more activities of daily living (referred to in the profession as ADLs)—bathing, dressing, eating, toileting, or transferring from a bed to a chair. Medicare pays for short-term skilled nursing care, under prescribed restrictions explained more completely in chapter 2. If your loved one needs only intermediate care, but may need skilled care in the future, make sure the homes you investigate offer both.

We are beginning to learn much about how to improve the lives of those suffering dementia in the nursing home setting. An attempt to make the surroundings more "homey" by using color, interesting wallpaper, and pleasant furniture is under way in some homes. The "Eden Alternative" and the "Human Habitat" are concepts beginning to be embraced by designers of nursing homes. These incorporate such things as children, pets, birds, plants, gardening, and bread baking into the daily living patterns of the residents, giving them responsibilities and choices about the use of their time. It is a good sign of creative and caring people trying to make a positive difference in the lives of those who need nursing home care.

A visit to any facility conveys much about the care your loved one would receive. Ask several family members to visit as many nursing homes as possible with you. These should be accessible and the costs within your ability to pay. Some nursing homes establish units or floors with a specially trained staff to give support and care to mentally impaired residents. Such an environment provides a higher ratio of staff to residents and greater freedom of movement. One experienced friend suggests visiting no fewer than three and no more than five homes. For the first visit come unannounced. Take the following list with you to each visit and compare the results. Having identified the home that seems best, make several visits at different times on different days. Investigate the following criteria:

- Does the facility have a list of references? Does it look and smell clean? Is it in good repair?
- Is it licensed by the state or a local agency and accredited by the Joint Commission on Accreditation of Hospitals? Does the local ombudsman (outside patient/family advocate) visit the facility regularly?
- How large is the staff? How are they relating to the residents? Does the staff include a physician and a nurse around the clock? Are there activities and programs involving patients outside their rooms? Outdoors? Is there a safe place for AD patients to pace?
- Visiting hours: When are they? Who can come?
- What arrangements are made for medical care, including dental, foot, and eye care?
- How many beds to a room? Can personal belongings be brought? What happens if roommates don't get along? Is there a window in each room? Is there room for wheelchairs in the halls and dining rooms to move around easily? Is the lighting appropriate? Are there private areas for visits with family or physicians?
- How are meals handled for those who cannot go to the dining room or who are unable to feed themselves? What about special diets? If possible go at meal time to visit with someone who has a loved one in the home. If not, introduce yourself to a visiting family member. Explain your need for objective information and ask them your questions. Most people fully understand your turmoil and will be generously cooperative. They may even invite you to meet their loved one and observe for yourself. Is the food appetizing: hot foods, hot; cold foods, cold? Check for weekly menus. Do they correspond with what is being served?
- How is laundry handled? Does it cost extra?
- Are residents treated with dignity or talked down to like children? Does the staff know the residents' names and respect their need for privacy?
- Do residents wear their own clothes? Are they kept clean and well groomed? What about hair care? Does that cost extra?
- Are community volunteers involved with residents? How?
- Is there any physical therapy, occupational therapy, or recreation for the mentally impaired? How often? This is an extremely important issue, particularly in homes where the mentally impaired are placed in restraining chairs.

- If you observe residents in restraining chairs, how tight are the restraints?
- Do the residents appear to be happy? Do any appear frightened?
- Does the building have a sprinkler system and clearly posted fire emergency exit routes?
- Check for safety features such as grab bars in bathrooms, in hallways, and in elevators. Do call lights work? Are calls for assistance responded to promptly?
- What does all this cost? What are considered extra costs? Is this home certified for and willing to accept Medicaid patients? If a private-pay patient's money runs out, will the home continue to care for the person on Medicaid until their death? If the response is positive to this question, get it in writing (see below). If a patient should leave a home, are there refunds on advance payments? Is the family informed when charges are increased? Is any of this cost covered by a patient's insurance? Getting a signed statement about specifics of cost protects against surprises. Higher costs do not always guarantee better care.
- Ask to see the Patient Bill of Rights required of every institution.
- Participate vigorously in the development of your loved one's individual care plan upon admission. Though handled in many places as burdensome paperwork required by law, this plan is your reference for care received in the months ahead. Reforms governing nursing homes were made by Congress in 1987 (the Omnibus Reconciliation Act [OBRA]) mandating certified nursing homes not only to maintain but also promote and enhance each patient's quality of life, and to supply services and activities that help each patient achieve and maintain his or her "highest practicable physical, mental and psychosocial well-being."[2]

Experience shows that the answers to these questions cannot always be depended upon as truthful.[3] But they should be asked. One learns much from acute observation. That's why several family members should go to visit. Pool your impressions but keep in mind the admonitions in our discussion of day-care centers: Make judgments based on the way the needs of your loved one will be met, not on your needs as a healthy, functioning adult. The size, ability, and motivation of the staff are the most important factors in determining the quality of care.[4] Summaries of nursing home inspections are available to you upon request in local health and welfare offices.

In general, nursing homes represent a lucrative business we have subsidized since the advent of Medicare and Medicaid. Use great caution before signing a contract that requires you to turn over your life savings for life care. Incentive for providing service diminishes the longer the patient lives. Check with your State Department of Health and Welfare to see if such contracts are legal in your state. If so, have a lawyer read the contract before you sign it.

In 1998 the news is bleak, and fears rise for Medicaid patients. Blame is being leveled on all sides of a difficult situation, given the rapid rise of our elderly population. "Across the country, HMOs [and some major nursing home companies] are starting to abandon their poorest patients [after] having embraced Medicaid patients in the early 1990s.... One big reason: State legislatures have reduced the per-member monthly rates they pay HMOs.... State Medicaid directors counter that the big for-profit HMOs are to blame for abandoning a business they didn't run well.... Patient advocates worry that Medicaid clients will be thrown back to so-called Medicaid mills—small clinics that generate revenue from high patient volume—letting care suffer and costs soar again."[5]

Fearing legislative investigations into fraud and abuse, lawsuits holding the nursing home company to "ever higher standards of care it can't sustain under Medicaid rates," and desirous of the wealthier patients, some nursing homes are evicting their Medicaid residents. Big companies are "racing into the nursing home industry and pursuing more aggressive pricing strategies...targeting the higher end of the market."[6] All this makes it important to know your rights. If your loved one on Medicaid is told suddenly that they are to be discharged immediately from the nursing home, or that Medicare payment stops here—today— use the telephone from the hospital or nursing home to challenge the discharge or lowered level of care determination. Ask for reconsideration in writing. Don't accept the response, "They're not improving." The law states that if you require these skilled care services, you are due them. Notice of ineligibility for Medicare must be made in writing. Hopefully, these thorny problems can be gradually worked out, easing the burden of families. Knowing the difficulties ahead of time will make your choices of nursing home care more satisfying, the questions you ask more efficient, and life for your loved one more pleasant.

Be clear about extra charges; for example, although nursing homes buy drugs in bulk, individual patients and Medicaid are frequently charged more than a person who buys a single prescription at the pharmacy. Once your loved one is admitted, go over the bills carefully, and don't hesitate to challenge services billed that were not rendered or items for which you feel you or Medicaid is being overcharged.

Be alert to overdrugged residents sitting passively as though asleep but with their eyes open. If the policy "to be good is to be quiet" describes the general atmosphere, look elsewhere for more alertness, activity, and mobility among the residents.[7]

Because many state laws prohibit locked doors in nursing homes, some homes use restraining chairs for memory-impaired residents. Fear of patients falling becomes a liability and safety issue for them. Some states are changing this law to allow secure areas for such residents to move about freely. One member of my AD support group, concerned that her father was immobilized for long hours every day, bought him a rocking chair. Though still restrained, the rocking gives him comfort as well as some exercise.

Families tend to fret about the frequency of showers or baths for their loved one. Immersion in water is a frightening experience for most memory-impaired people. It is not uncommon for homes to provide daily sponge baths and weekly showers or tub baths. Routine, also, is the administering of tranquilizers prior to the bath. Perhaps all concerned would be best served by holding to the criteria of general cleanliness: healthy skin condition, lack of odor, and clean clothing.

I asked the question, "What do families tend to do that complicates your job?" The social worker on the staff of a large, well-run nursing home replied, "A month or two following admission, families, now rested, begin to forget the difficulties and demands this job places on those giving care. They become unrealistic in their expectations and complaints begin. That a patient gets a bath only once a week, for example, is more a problem of the visiting spouse who still bathes every day or so than of the resident whose personal hygiene is now managed differently."

If you are disturbed by the quality of care your loved one is getting, speak first with the charge nurse on the floor. If that does not help the situation, go to the director of nurses. If the home has a social worker on staff, discuss the problem with her. It's her job to listen to the family.

Knowing there are two sides to every problem, she will attempt to resolve the difficulty by working with both staff and family. The nursing home administrator is the ultimate authority for resolution. Failing that, if you haven't already done so, inquire at your local Department on Aging about an ombudsman for the elderly. Many states have such patient advocates who can handle complaints confidentially without disclosing the name of the resident or complainant. If all else fails, do not be afraid to remove your loved one from one care facility and into another that meets more adequately the needs as you can best assess them.

Nursing homes encourage visits. Two of the women in our support group go frequently to feed their husbands lunch. They look in on and visit with each other, sharing a camaraderie that is helpful to all.

According to Dr. Barry Reisberg, respected authority in this field, a loved one who has reached the most advanced stages of AD, unable to speak or communicate, benefits from the presence of family and friends. Seeing familiar faces and hearing their voices triggers emotional responses in the brain, bringing a degree of quality to the life of the afflicted one. Visiting regularly also keeps the staff alert to your interest in the level of care they provide.

Having noted the preceding cautions, remember the excruciatingly difficult task of those who give the care we have searched for so painstakingly. Express appreciation to the staff whenever you can. You know better than most people the demands made on them. Although you may encounter hard and unsympathetic employees who grimly do just enough to get by, you can be grateful for the many caring, loving people who serve in our behalf. They free us to resume life once again.

Sons and daughters of the AD afflicted, don't let your sensitivity become a cop-out. In the course of my interviews with caregivers, I've heard something like this many times: "My son helped me the day we admitted my husband into the nursing home, but he never could stand to come see his father again." When a weary woman facing strange and difficult legal decisions alone was asked about her children and the help they might give, she sighed and said, "My son help? He's too sensitive. It has made him weak." Seeing a parent in a helpless and noncommunicative condition, old, weak, ugly (by our standards), forces us to face our own death. Yes, it is difficult, but be encouraged to do it. Just like the work of coming to terms with difficult memories, it's work that will haunt you until you accomplish it.

After you place your loved one in a home, you will continue to need your support group for some time. Feelings of guilt and anxiety erupt: This might happen to me someday. I feel guilty for feeling so relieved. Will they really take good care of him? They don't love him like I do. She will be so much more confused now and angry at me. That look she gives me, like she thought she'd never see me again—as though I had run out on her—hits me right in the gut every time. She may even die sooner because I didn't keep her here at home. What if he lives ten or fifteen more years? How am I going to pay? If it all goes and Medicaid finally does pay, I'll have so little left. How will I live?

Haunted by such thoughts and the grief of that final separation, a wife painfully recalled her memories of the first weeks. "I felt numb all over—almost dead for the first ten days or so. Now I'm beginning to feel life coming back with energy. I'm making contact with friends and feel like doing things again. It's wonderful to be alive."

These thoughts and emotions pursue everyone who has gone through the trauma of admitting a loved one into a nursing home. It takes courage to resist giving in to the mental and emotional whirlpool you feel yourself almost literally being sucked into. Use your support group. Use your family, friends, minister, doctor, counselor, therapist, or anyone who can stand by you through this period of numb grief.

Our support group has begun to encourage a subgroup of those who have recently admitted a loved one into a nursing home. One member wisely made it clear that this was not a time to gather to complain, moan, and find fault with the way their loved ones were being cared for by the nursing home staff. This small group, who are painfully aware of the feelings of the primary caregiver, can now minister to those who have made application and wait in that limbo of terrible dread and hope for the call from admissions. Such a gesture of caring for and sharing with others begins to stimulate the green and growing signs of new life and energy.

It is no mark of courage to handle this alone. It takes courage to ask for help even though doing so may seem even more complicating than solitary determined perseverance. Accept with gratitude whatever support and friendship is offered you. Know that even as you suffer, you are in training for the day when you can help another through this ordeal. Hopefully you will begin to realize that you hold within the power of your own experience a gift for those just beginning their pilgrimage on this difficult way. Such a gift was given me in a quiet discussion about the difficult decision concerning autopsy.

## CLARIFYING CONFUSIONS ABOUT AUTOPSY

Over a leisurely dinner I listened to the story of a strikingly graceful woman whose husband died in the prime of life from complications of AD. A dynamic man who had used his brilliant energies to manage a major corporation, he spent his last days in a nursing home, finally slipping into a coma. "At the time of his death I was asked to approve an autopsy with the idea of donating his brain for AD research. It was just too much. I was so distressed. Without giving it thought, I refused on the grounds that he had already suffered far too much. Two years have slipped by now, and I find myself dwelling more on the happy times, the good memories rather than the ordeal of his final years. I regret my last decision. If someone had helped me think it through ahead of time, I feel certain I would have agreed. In fact, he would have insisted on it himself in the earlier years, had we known enough to discuss it and make the arrangements."

It may seem inconceivable for you at this reading to consider choices and decisions surrounding the question of autopsy. Yet this option should be examined thoroughly prior to the emotional trauma following the death of a loved one.

What is required for a family to make such a decision wisely and well? I called the Alzheimer's Association and asked for the Autopsy Assistant Network Representative in my state. The representative was a kind and knowledgeable source of information. Upon request, he sent a helpful brochure and other general information on autopsy. Such a representative is available in every state to work with you.

I asked my family physician about procedure for autopsy and possible donation of brain specimen. Since he had seldom been confronted with this question, he referred me to the Pathology Department at Bridgeport Hospital, Bridgeport, Connecticut. There I spoke with Dr. George Kleinman, a neuropathologist, who was most helpful. "Procedure differs among hospitals and states. An autopsy, done at any hospital, can be restricted in any way; e.g., the family can request that it be limited to the brain only. Keep in mind that an autopsy procedure never disfigures the body. If a family desires funeral services with an open casket, an autopsy does not interfere with these wishes. However, many funeral directors discourage autopsy as it costs them more to prepare the body for viewing. Many physicians, as well, are not positively disposed to autopsy. They do not appreciate the value of the learning they gain from this procedure. This attitude is perhaps a reflection on the institutions where physicians are trained. Consequently, the family may have to press for autopsy in some cases. The question of donating brain specimens for research requires constant assessment based upon the current need for such tissue at the national AD research centers. The family physician should contact the neuropathologist at the hospital where the physician has privileges. Such inquiry is usually welcomed. Both pathologist and family physician should be supportive of the donor family, particularly the surviving spouse."

"What is done during and after autopsy?" I asked.

"This varies according to both hospital procedure and methodology established by the receiving research groups. Generally, the neuropathologist prepares the brain by dividing it in half. Half is frozen for biochemical studies, half is preserved. The body is returned to the funeral director. The entire brain is sent to the nearest national Alzheimer study group. The national group sends a follow-up report to the submitting neuropathologist, who will report to the family physician. As these reports are extremely technical, the family physician serves to interpret them to the family."

"What does all this cost?" I questioned.

"Prices and policy vary from hospital to hospital. Many hospitals charge nothing if the donor has ever been treated there or is a patient of a staff physician. If the patient dies in a nursing home, the family usually pays the cost of transportation to the hospital for autopsy and then to the funeral home."[8]

"In addition to advancing the discovery of cause or cure for AD, is there any other reason a family may wish to request a brain autopsy?"

"Until there is a procedure for positive diagnosis of AD, autopsy remains the only way for families concerned about genetic implications to know with any certainty that they have indeed been dealing with AD. A recent example of this in our practice was the surprising evidence upon autopsy of Parkinsonian dementia, not AD at all."

June A. White, worker in dementia research for fifteen years and coauthor with Dr. Leonard L. Heston of *Dementia: A Practical Guide to Alzheimer's Disease and Related Illnesses*, urges complete autopsy. "Autopsy for the purpose of positive diagnosis and confirmation of AD is the most important reason for autopsy, but people do not die of AD. They die of some other cause, such as pneumonia, complicated by AD. Autopsy reveals the cause of death and provides families with such information as the health of lungs, heart, and arteries as well. This certain knowledge is the last gift AD-afflicted persons can give their children and grandchildren."[9]

# PART 2

# THE HUMAN RESPONSE

*Even memory is not necessary for love.*
*There is a land of the living and*
*a land of the dead, and the bridge is love,*
*the only survival, the only meaning.*

—THORNTON WILDER

# 1 0     A GROWING SERENITY

We lounged on the floating dock at the lake's edge behind our home enjoying the heightened pleasure that comes from conversation with newly arrived houseguests. As we watched the changing color of the sun playing shadows among the trees on the far bank, Dad spoke quietly: "Just look at the beauty that surrounds us here." He paused, obviously wanting to take it in deeply. "I'm reminded of passages in Ronald Wells's book you sent us. He writes about . . . oh, what is it he calls them, these moments when we are able to set ourselves apart from the activities that catch us up so in life . . . the worries and distractions that seem to keep us wound up with our own concerns . . . and just take a moment to stop and look about us for something . . . gifts we can see as beautiful, and from God, and be grateful. It was a good term he used, new to me."[1]

Unable to recall the precise words, he went on. "One of the gifts we've enjoyed day after day down in our park in Florida is that royal poinciana tree just across from our patio." Mother listened as though concentrating on his words would help her recall where they had been, this place he called "our park." Her forehead wrinkled with the effort to remember.

"Your mother and I watch it gradually become transformed from the barren branches you see when you visit in February into thousands of buds, then become a magnificent display of color, a cloudburst of reddish orange that stays for weeks, drops its blossoms, then begins to put out another batch of buds which open for us to delight in for many more weeks." Then thoughtfully, "It helps me see life in a better perspective."

He was in a talkative mood, pleased to have an exchange of conversation. Proud, I think, that within a week of his seventy-seventh birthday he had made the fifteen-hundred-mile trip driving from Florida to Connecticut without unusual difficulty.

"I'll tell you something else I'm daily grateful for. That's the pleasure and good exercise we get from swimming. We're finding that your mother is more comfortable now in the pool than in the ocean, but as long as she has her mask and snorkel gear on, I don't worry about her. The beauty we've seen beneath the water! All kinds of animal and plant life, fascinating and marvelous."

Then he turned philosophic and spoke as he would have spoken even had no one but the trees been there to listen. "It's becoming more and more amazing to me the older I get that somehow, somewhere down the course of our lives, what seemed to be a period of great adversity seems later to pay great dividends in ways we could never have imagined."

I was curious about what was coming, amazed at these continued words of gratitude, ashamed of my own thoughts of sometimes seeing their visit as an added burden to my already busy life.

"Do you remember when you were in high school how I used to get those paralyzing headaches?"

"Of course. How could any of us forget that?"

"My doctor finally prescribed swimming three times a week. So I began going to the YMCA pool to swim on my lunch hour. Then I took lessons in snorkeling and began to truly enjoy it. I told your mother one day that if she'd take lessons I would take her on vacation, camping in the Virgin Islands, where we could snorkel in warm water on ocean reefs. She got busy and learned. From then on, we did just that for a number of years, as you know. You see? Because snorkeling has been a part of her life pattern for so long, she's still able to swim safely. It gives me the chance for good exercise too. Now, if I'd never had those pesky headaches..." (A year later Mother became afraid and refused to go into the water. This was the end of swimming for Dad for the duration of her life. Undaunted, he regularly took her along to the tennis court, where she paced nearby while he hit twenty-five balls over the net, retrieved them, and hit them again until his exercise needs were met.)

Mother sat listening peacefully, relaxed into the present, enjoying the shared moment of beauty in her own way, commenting several times about the differences in the shades of green of the trees. She soon began to hum softly, a crooked tune which took me several moments to decipher. It was one of the melodies, as a child, I had often heard her sing contentedly at the kitchen sink while she prepared dinner: "Amazing Grace."

For the moment on this rainy day, I find contentment in seeing Dad able to read without interruption. Mother is as happy as she can be, splashing at the kitchen sink with the silver cleaner, silverware, and warm sudsy water, and I work at writing even as the story unfolds.

## A DEEPENING FAITH

"You know, Dad, sooner or later when you're faced with something as devastating as this disease, you have to come to terms with the how and why questions." We sat after breakfast enjoying the quiet mood following a morning rain. "People of faith, I've discovered, wrestle just as hard as those who proclaim no faith. Sometimes harder, it seems. It's tough to wrap our idea of a loving Creator around the ugly reality of what's happening to Mother and what that does to us. We've always been taught that God has a plan for us. Surely you don't see this as part of God's plan for Mother?"

"Wait a minute, don't rush by one big thought and into another. I can't compute that fast!" We smiled. I waited, knowing it would be worth the wait. "You say it's tough to . . . how did you put it . . . wrap our idea of a loving God around what's happening to your mother and me? I find God wrapped about us more and more each day. I can't imagine living now without that warmth and protection.

"Do I see this as part of God's plan? The disease? No. I believe God will be first in line applauding the researchers who discover the cause for this disease and how we can prevent or cure it. Neither can I expect God to perform some magical cure, although I have come to believe in recent years in the possibility of miracles. The challenge I see that fits into this idea of a plan for our lives is purely and simply what we do with what we've been given, no ifs, ands, or buts."

"As kind and loving as Mother has always been, how do you explain it?" I persisted, my own need to know stubbornly asserting itself, still wrestling with the "why her?" question. "Does it have to do with good and evil? Where does evil come from? Is God the author of both?"

"You sound like the Grand Inquisitor."[2] Dad looked at me with patient amusement. "It helps to be seventy-seven. It's easier to live without insisting on all the answers. You're asking me questions that have been posed since the beginning of time.

"First of all, you need to get over the idea that we earn our way to the 'good' life by being, as you say, kind and loving. It just doesn't work that way.

"Does it have to do with good and evil? Does any disease have any relation to good and evil? I don't know. It may. Do I explain evil by describing it as some bogeyman spirit that has gotten inside your mother's head? No." He paused, leaned his elbows on the table, fingertips together, deep in thought. "I believe God is the Creator of the world and all that is in it; light and darkness, good and evil.

"How else would we grow and learn, become stronger and better? Let's imagine, for instance, even if we could snap our fingers and do away with..."—he paused, searching for an example—"dishonesty. Think of the billions of dollars that could be diverted to good purposes if there were no such thing. Yet, if we were deprived of the choice of being honest or dishonest, could you call that good? We just don't know the answers to these questions."

He sat thinking for a moment. "Yet what it all boils down to in my book, what makes me able to believe so completely in a loving Creator who wants the best for us yet allows us to struggle with life's difficulties, is the immense difference holding to that belief makes in the transformed life of an individual. Think for a minute about the people in your life experience who have allowed themselves to become bitter and hostile toward God and others because of circumstances they may pronounce as unfair or cruel. Then think of those who experience the same kinds of hurts and struggles, maybe even worse ones, but who respond to them in positive ways, making the best out of what seems to be an impossible situation. Such a response is an effort toward becoming... complete."

Suddenly I knew what my father meant by being complete. I glanced at the perpetual calendar that sits on my kitchen counter and read for the second time that morning Martin Luther's quote: "A Christian is never in a state of completion, but always in the process of becoming." To listen to my father, whose entire life has been so drastically altered, speak fervently in God's behalf was powerful. Remembering past episodes of his flaring temper and how quickly my own patience with Mother disintegrated despite my efforts to stay calm, I thought this idea of becoming complete seemed something worth exploring.

"Remember the verse that Jesus is given credit for?" I queried. "'You, therefore, must be perfect as your heavenly Father is perfect' (Matt. 5:48). For this Christian, that instruction is enough to cause me to throw in the towel if it's read without knowing the Greek origin of the word 'perfect.' *Teleos.* It means 'complete.'[3] It fits with what you're talking about. 'You therefore must be complete even as your heavenly Father is complete.' That verse made me feel guilty and discouraged until I learned that—only recently."

Dad nodded in silent consideration. "I suppose the Jew has similar teachings to grapple with. It's amazing when you think what there is to learn in the process of becoming complete, and the possibilities of living life that way. Wouldn't you say so, Dear?" He addressed Mother, who had tired of the conversation and had been roaming about the house probably wondering where she was. She seemed pleased to discover us there and sat down again.

"Would you like a piece of toast?" she replied.

"Why, we've just had our breakfast."

"We did?"

"Don't tell me you're still hungry!"

"Well, I could eat another piece," she said, eyeing the jelly.

"You're the limit," he responded affectionately.

I observe Mother and think about the various stories from my acquaintances who struggle with a wide spectrum of behavior on the part of their brain-damaged loved ones. It makes me wonder if at some point, particularly in the deterioration we see in some Alzheimer's victims, we are witnessing the destruction or shedding of the persona, the mask which has informed behavior throughout life.[4] As the persona deteriorates, we see in increasingly exaggerated ways a return to expressions of the exposed and unrestrained ego.

Mother's personality as an adult was always fairly placid, gentle, easygoing. She played the role of peacemaker in raising four children. She dealt with a domineering husband capable of rigid perfectionism and explosively angry reactions to displeasing situations. To see her respond now to some of his curt demands with tongue stuck out, her hands flapping at either ear in an uncharacteristic go-to-hell stance is unnerving. Her behavior is simply an honest response to unwanted demands. Yet most often she moves easily into cooperative and manageable behavior. To imagine their roles reversed is a staggering thought, fearsome in its implications.

I strongly believe she has continued efforts at communication because she is treated with dignity and respect, not ignored or ridiculed. We respond to her repeated questions and confusion as much as possible with considerate and patient answers. I don't suggest that all is calm, all is bright. We hear occasional bellows of impatient irritation from the bedroom or bathroom, where my father insists on including her in the responsibilities of bathing, dressing, and bed making. This often requires directing her every move. But he persists, refusing to give in and do for her those most basic human tasks. I believe he sees her continued involvement as crucial to maintaining a connecting thread that will bind her in her own mind to the rest of humanity.

The caregiver needs to ventilate feelings of hostility and pain, which can build up to insufferable limits at times. Outcries of anger and frustration can be extremely upsetting to family members who visit or who are visited if they do not understand this necessity. I thought of this recently when our minister, speaking of the *via negativa,* those times in our lives when we are at our wits' end, tipped back his head, his arms flailing in midair, and shrieked. A gut-wrenching wail of agony. A quiet pause. "Amen," he said, explaining that this is the most ancient prayer we can pray.

Adjusting to the loss of the persona one has lived with for an entire marriage or lifetime is no small task. It imposes changes in one's own "mask." Such transformations cost dearly in emotional expenditure. It is important for friends, family, and caregiver alike to acknowledge the depth and cause of such feelings and not be sent into extremes of dismay or guilt over them. An anguished bellow now and then is a quick and simple way of releasing those feelings. One of the few benefits that comes with memory-impairing diseases is that such outcries are immediately forgotten.

# 11   RELIEF THROUGH HUMOR

A SENSE OF HUMOR can help us get through even the worst of times. My father's innate sense of humor has not only remained intact, it is developing. One Saturday morning he was in high spirits when I talked to him on the phone. "I want you to know I woke up this morning with a woman named Marilyn next to me."

"You did?" I chuckled. "You mean Marilyn Monroe? Wow! How did that feel?"

"Well, it was quite remarkable. She even had on one of your mother's nightgowns."

"Really! Now that's amazing!"

"No, the amazing thing is... they look so much alike!" I could hear Mother laugh.

Sometimes it is her childlike responses that bring healing laughter. On my parents' visit with us in 1985 they frequently sat together by the lake behind our home. Dad reported that Mother continually worried about where they would stay, when and where they would eat and sleep. (Though such questions were frequent even at home, this is an example of added confusion caused by their pattern of travels to visit.)

"I told her, 'Now listen, Dear. You don't need to fret that way. I've told you we should enjoy the beauty around us and the good things we have, and put our faith and trust in God. He'll take care of what we need.' She put me in my place when she said, 'But he might forget.'"

While hustling Mother around the several blocks they walk on their visits with us, they approach the foot of the hills and Mother begins to complain, "Do we have to walk up this hill?" His response varies. "Well, we have two choices. We can either walk up the hill or lie down and roll up. Which would you rather do?" She responds enthusiastically, "Let's walk up." "Then, let's get going." He constantly demands, "Pick up those feet. Swing those arms! Don't lag behind."

I walked with them one day and as we huffed up the last hill Mother dragged behind a bit. "It's like the little engine that could, isn't it, Mom?" I suggested.

"She's doing fine," Dad encouraged. "Aren't you, Dear?"

"Yep," she puffed.

"She's got a lot of spunk, that girl. She does real well."

Their walks pay great dividends. It's an activity she sometimes initiates. Dad consistently praises her when she cooperates. At other times, she refuses to walk more than a short distance. I believe the result of this disciplined approach is her continued ability to walk freely without the typical stooped Alzheimer shuffle. The walks also help her sleep at night.

Each morning the question is repeated, "What are we going to do today?" Dad and I both respond with a variety of answers: "One thing at a time...we have lots to do...maybe we'll go for a ride...errands." I overheard him one morning after this breakfast ritual humming snatches of "It's a Long Way to Tipperary" while he mended a screen. Standing nearby, Mother repeated the question. "What are we going to do today?"

"The best we can. That's all a horse can do...the best we can." Mother said, "Okay," and that seemed to settle it for a while.

Conversation with the afflicted person becomes a challenge in the later stages. There are days when Mother has no idea who Charles is or who we are, yet she still wants to help with any meal preparation. Her sense of identity with kitchen habits and responsibility lingers. Trying to engage her in helping to make an apple salad, I asked, "Do you get many apples in Florida?" She turned to Dad and repeated the question as best she could remember it. "Apples?" he queried, "Heavens, yes! We have apple-plexies all the time."

After they returned to their Florida mobile home in the fall of 1984, I telephoned them, curious to know how Mother had readjusted. Change in surroundings aggravates disorientation, and such extended trips are not generally recommended. Dad was willing to pay the price of coping with her confusion so they could enjoy a change of climate and have time with the extended family. He was pleased to be back, and Mother commented that it was a nice place and she'd like to stay there. However, a day later she began repeatedly asking when they were leaving. "I guess I got a little exasperated," Dad admitted. "I finally told her, 'Now listen! You just remember it this way. If you get pregnant tonight you'll have time to give birth to a child before we leave here!' She thought that was pretty funny."

In one of his letters he wrote: "There is one particular tree your mother notices often on one of our favorite walks. I always remind her how we're going to build a tree house in it when we get young enough. She usually gets a chuckle out of that, but the last time she replied, 'That's not very likely.'"

Wherever Mother goes she seems to search for things that "don't belong" on the ground or floor. She grooms the floor, rug, driveway, and sidewalk. Her pockets become a treasure of the most peculiar junk. She fingered a plastic doll's leg retrieved from one of their walks. "Where did this come from?" she asked Dad. He frowned, then replied, "That must be your legacy."

Language difficulties that twist Mother's speech are emerging. We laugh when we can. To her a tree bare of leaves is a "tree full of nothing." A sign "Flowers for Sale" is read "Lovers for Sale." A year later she still hummed "Amazing Grace" as we walked about their park. "I keep getting this tune in my mind," she puzzled. "Sing it for me," I told her. She couldn't manage any of the words without help. We sang through the hymn. A few minutes later a large truck pulled up and parked along the highway just outside the fence. Mother said quite seriously, "Do you suppose that truck is full of amazing grace?" "I'm sure of it," I answered.

Every time we went out in the car Mother pointed with fresh excitement to the tall power towers; some had osprey nests atop them. "Look at that tall thing! What do you suppose that is? That a bird's nest up there?" One time Dad responded, "There certainly is a substantial mass of sticks and twigs. I guess we could say the birds go to high mass up there." This amused Dad and me as he gave me one of his long looks. "I've discovered that I can turn a lot of annoying questions around and defuse many pesky situations when I try to make something funny of it. It's a form of mental relief for me even when your mother doesn't get it."

On one visit I wandered into their bedroom when Dad was putting Mother to bed. Patting her with bath powder, he told her, "There! I'm really giving you the treatment tonight. I'll think I'm sleeping with the Queen of Sheba." Rather than return a smile, her somber lost look seemed to speak from some interior depth of locked-in feeling. "Good night, Dear." He kissed her gently. "Good night."

In January 1985 my trip to visit them was hurriedly rescheduled when I learned how sick Dad was with a cold and flu. After he had been in bed for nearly two weeks, Mother began to understand vaguely that something was wrong with Charles. Prior to that time, she'd been quite indignant every time she looked for him and found him lying in bed. One day she went into the bedroom, lay down, and put her head lovingly on his chest. He stroked her hair gently and to his beloved transplanted farm girl from Kansas, he said, "Well, Dear, I guess you'll have to do the milking this morning."

He got up several mornings later feeling better. He started toward the bathroom and Mother followed. He turned to her with a sparkle of the old mischievous humor in his eye and pronounced with dignity, "I'm going in here to shake the dew off the lily." He closed the door behind him gently. She looked at me and said, "Nothing can get him down . . . where's Charles?" I told her. Softly, so he wouldn't hear, she inquired, "Do you suppose a man like him ever gets married?"

"You've been married to him for fifty-three years," I smiled.

"I have?" she asked. "Then I guess I don't need to worry."

## Beyond Depression

What else is meant by "the human response" to this ghastly affliction that so changes our lives? We have learned some practical and positive ways to cope and respond. It is also human to be dreadfully discouraged.

M. Scott Peck speaks of the healthiness of depression. He defines it as the "feeling associated with giving up something loved . . . or at least something that is a part of ourselves and familiar. . . . Since mentally healthy human beings must grow, and since giving up or loss of the old self is an integral part of the process of mental and spiritual growth, depression is a normal and basically healthy phenomenon. It becomes abnormal or unhealthy only when something interferes with the giving-up process with the result that the depression is prolonged" and the completion of the giving-up process cannot be resolved.[1] Psychologists often describe this as being stuck, this inability to move on with life. It's a temptation to give in to a state of helplessness that requires the strength of some other person or agency to come to our rescue.

However, it is also human to search for the unknown strength that has been forming deep within throughout our lives. We may be surprised at the power of this strength, this goodness within.

In his sobering book on the power of evil, Peck observes: "Stress is the test for goodness. The truly good are they who in time of stress do not desert their integrity, their maturity, their sensitivity.... Nobility might be defined as the capacity not to regress in response to degradation, not to become blunted in the face of pain, to tolerate the agonizing and remain intact.... One measure and perhaps the best measure of a person's greatness is their capacity for suffering."[2]

Though we have much in common, we must recognize that each person who walks this path with a mentally impaired loved one does so in a way never before experienced by another. I write about my father's response because I know it intimately. I am a part of it. My brother and sisters, also involved, would write about it quite differently. I am convinced, however, that this disciplined man represents many unsung, unknown heroes who respond to their own situations with similar patient, steadfast striving.

To compare the human response of others with that of one person is to sit in audacious judgment. Too many factors influence the impact on the afflicted one and thus on the caregiver: age of onset (those in their forties and fifties present the caregiver with dreadful choices about how to provide care while they continue to hold jobs and live fully themselves), rapidity of deterioration, basic personality (placid, aggressive), drastic personality changes, physical health and strength of both afflicted and caregiver, availability and use of support systems such as day-care centers, home health care, respite, and involvement of family and friends. The list is long.

Marshall Cheney says it beautifully with her sensitive words of wisdom. "You are not a bad caregiver because you got angry last week. It is important to recognize that you have real limitations, both physical and mental, and that this disease will probably exceed them both. You are devoting yourself to providing the best care you can give to the person you love, but you are not perfect and you will need help. You will also make mistakes. What is important to help yourself and the person you care for is that you understand when you need help and get it."[3]

The measure of goodness or nobility should not be made against the moment of decision to admit one's inability to continue in the role of primary caregiver. We mustn't begin to gauge ourselves by questioning others: "How long were you able to keep him or her at home?" The role of suffering caregiver, even after admitting a loved one into a nursing home, continues until the end. Our job is to remain intact so that when we are relieved of our primary responsibilities as caregiver we can move on in life.

# 12     A CALL TO SAINTHOOD

*Life, what have you done to me?*
*As o'er the sea the sun sinks ever faster,*
*as if it moved towards the darkness,*
*so does your image sink and sink and sink*
*without a pause*
*into the ocean of the past. . . .*
*I feel that everything around me, over, under me*
*is smiling at me, unmoved, enigmatic,*
*smiling at my hopeless efforts*
*to grasp the wind,*
*to capture what has gone. . . .*
*I want my life; I claim my own life back again,*
*my past, yourself.*
*Yourself. A tear wells up and fills my eye;*
*can I, in mists of tears,*
*regain your image,*
*yourself entire?*
*But I will not weep;*
*only the strong are helped by tears,*
*weaklings they make ill.*

—DIETRICH BONHOEFFER,
EXCERPT FROM "THE PAST"[1]

Dietrich Bonhoeffer, a remarkable young German theologian, was imprisoned by Hitler's regime for two years before he was executed at the age of thirty-nine. Author of this melancholy yet poignant poem, he could have been writing as a caregiver to a loved one lost to the ravages of brain disease. Clearly, he felt the deepest despair as he wrote to his fiancée and used his poetry to acknowledge such feelings. Perhaps he understood what we are told today, that repression of such deep feeling is decidedly unhealthy.

Bonhoeffer has much to say to us through his books *The Cost of Discipleship* and *Letters and Papers from Prison.* I read and reread the following passages from *Letters:*

> For the calmness and joy with which we meet what is laid on us are as infectious as the terror that I see among the people here at each new attack. Indeed I think such an attitude gives one the greatest authority provided it is genuine and natural and not merely for show. People need some constant factor to guide them. We are [not] daredevils, but that has nothing to do with the courage that comes with the grace of God. . . .

> Of course, not everything that happens is simply "God's will," and yet in the last resort nothing happens "without your Father's will" (Mt 10:29), i.e., through every event, however untoward, there is access to God.

> An outward and purely physical regime (exercises and a cold wash down in the morning) itself provides some support for one's inner discipline. Further, there is nothing worse in such times than to try to find a substitute for the irreplaceable. . . . I don't think it is good to talk to strangers about our condition; that always stirs up one's troubles. . . . Above all, we must never give way to self-pity.

> . . . the dearer and richer our memories, the more difficult the separation. But gratitude changes the pangs of memory into a tranquil joy. The beauties of the past are borne, not as a thorn in the flesh, but as a precious gift in themselves.

> I have learned here that the *facts* can always be mastered, and that difficulties are magnified out of all proportion simply by fear and anxiety. From the moment we wake until we fall asleep we must

commend other people wholly and unreservedly to God and leave them in his hands, and transform our anxiety for them into prayers on their behalf.

It is a strange feeling to see a man whose life has in one way or another been so intimately bound up with one's own for years going out to meet an unknown future about which one can do virtually nothing. I think this realization of one's own helplessness has . . . two sides—it brings both anxiety and relief. As long as we ourselves are trying to help shape someone else's destiny, we are never quite free of the question whether what we are doing is really for the other person's benefit—at least in any matter of great importance. But when all possibility of cooperating in anything is suddenly cut off, then behind any anxiety about him there is the consciousness that his life has now been placed wholly in better and stronger hands. For you, and for us, the greatest task during the coming weeks, and perhaps months, may be to entrust each other to those hands.[2]

Small wonder that so many considered this man as saintly.

Dr. Barry Reisberg in his lecture to a group of family members and caregivers of Alzheimer's victims observed, "To be a caregiver is a call to sainthood. Do you know the definition of a saint? One who labors lovingly on another's behalf with no word or gesture of appreciation nor any expectation of it."

But to be called to sainthood does not mean that we deny our feelings of depression, despair, and anger. Clearly, in his poem "The Past" Bonhoeffer shares with us his pain. Sharing the pain is our difficulty. The pen is perhaps the easiest instrument of such sharing, ventured by few and somehow incomplete, for it lacks the responsive ear and heart.

What does it do to us who live through the agony and exhaustion of caring for an afflicted one whom we love? There are as many different answers to that question as there are people who answer it. But as I read about and talk with people living the solutions as best they can, I am impressed with just that overwhelming reality. We meet the problems in the best way we know how, always looking, asking, hoping for better ways to make it work.

Nevertheless, I see patterns of response. This is where foundations of religious faith begin to emerge. For those who have a strong faith to sustain them in such a trial, the going is not easier but it seems to be different. We ask the same questions, suffer the same confusion in the absence of answers, agonize over our doubts, and sometimes wonder what good our faithfulness has been. In our heart of hearts, though, we know we are not alone.

It helps to understand our humanness when we acknowledge that we all operate in an inconsistent manner between the polarities of hostility and hospitality.[3] For the caregiver of a brain-damaged person, the extremes of both responses and all degrees in between can be a roller-coaster ride from hour to hour.

In this brief passage from his novel *The Notebook,* Nicholas Sparks captures a caregiver who learns how to modify these extremes.

The days were hard on both of us. I was an encyclopedia, an object without feeling, of the whos, whats and wheres in her life, when in reality it is the whys, the things I did not know and could not answer, that make it all worthwhile. She would stare at pictures of forgotten offspring, hold paintbrushes that inspired nothing, and read love letters that brought back no joy. She would weaken over the hours, growing paler, becoming bitter, and ending the day worse than when it began. Our days were lost, and so was she. And selfishly, so was I.

So I changed. I became Magellan or Columbus, an explorer in the mysteries of the mind, and I learned, bumbling and slow, but learning nonetheless what had to be done. And I learned what is obvious to a child. That life is simply a collection of little lives, each lived one day at a time. That each day should be spent finding beauty in flowers and poetry and talking to animals. That a day spent with dreaming and sunsets and refreshing breezes cannot be bettered. But most of all, I learned that life is about sitting on benches next to ancient creeks with my hand on her knee and sometimes, on good days, for falling in love.[4]

Most of us are faced with unrelenting and extended periods of time that drag in our task of caring, yet are harassed by the constant feeling of never getting enough done. Over the years, tumultuous emotional ups and downs are draining. Regular daily periods of prayer for strength and patience are invaluable oases of reassurance to put us back on the track toward the generous spirit of hospitality. Even so, we find we can still be ugly.

It's hard to face the ugliness within. Yet we must face it. That rock buried in the center of the heart that won't seem to soften, the resentment that simmers when we see another couple our age enjoying an apparently carefree life together—or if we are the son or daughter giving care, we seethe at our entrapment. We experience the drowning waves of misery and depression when we indulge in self-pity. Outright rage erupts and changes us into screaming tyrants as we bellow at this lost loved one who haunts us by the very living memory of what she or he used to be. Difficult? At times, impossible.

So we need all the help we can get. I have seen the changes wrought by what we might call the rhythm of reliance. By a regular turning and returning to God we acknowledge our hostilities, give up our weakness and pain to our Source of strength, seek those moments that we can be grateful for in our day, until we begin ever so slightly to live closer to that warm and generous ideal we know we are meant to be.

As I teach the Shaker melody "Simple Gifts" in words and graceful dance to children and adults, I am struck by the wisdom of which they speak.

> 'Tis a gift to be simple,
> 'tis a gift to be free,
> 'tis a gift to come round where we want to be,
> And when we've found ourselves in the place that's right
> We will be in the valley of love and delight.
>
> When true simplicity is gained,
> to bow and to bend we will not be ashamed.
> To turn, turn, will be our delight
> 'til by turning, turning we come 'round right.

Turning, turning, sustained and used up, renewed and expended, energized and depleted, hopeful and again devastated, cheerful and depressed, lively and joyless. But steadfast, we come 'round right; grateful that we can experience the good, the reassuring, the positive, the refreshing, even at the very instant of a heartrending cry or a silent turning 'round to God.

Regular prayer or Bible reading was not a part of my childhood family custom aside from saying grace, usually the same prayer repeated at dinnertime. In recent years I've become aware that my parents share a morning time of devotion. Even though my work involves me intimately with the church, I was never invited—when visiting or being visited—to participate in their morning time together with the Bible. They would simply dispense with their usual routine. Such reticence to share our experience of faith is more common than most of us want to admit.

This changed several years ago while I was visiting my parents in their Florida home. I had become more sensitive to the power and significance of routine for Mother—the daily rhythm of living—so I encouraged Dad to continue their morning routine whatever it might be. With some hesitation he reached for the Bible nearby and turned to one of the letters of Paul. "Your mother and I have been reading the New Testament this winter."

He began to read, now and then repeating a particularly difficult or meaningful passage, perhaps commenting to her, "Now if we could just remember that," or "Wouldn't the world be a different place if all of us lived by that wisdom?"

Mother sat quietly, attentively, or gazed out the window. Once in a while she interrupted with some question or an observation about something that seemed peculiar to her, often unrelated. When Dad finished the reading we discussed it at some length. I could sense his pleasure in having someone join him to grapple with the more difficult ideas.

As our discussion ended, another shy space opened between us. Dad reached for my hand and taking Mother's in his other, he asked gently, "Martha, will you lead us in prayer?" That quiet time of study and prayer began our day and week together in a way that illumined the power of faith for me. His morning prayers are spoken so earnestly, so humbly, and always with an expression of gratitude and trust. His petitions for forgiveness and strength to discern and carry forth God's will established the rhythm of reliance that made our time together more peaceful, our dealings with the frustrations more gentle. His ministry to me in sharing these private moments of turning to God served to strengthen me again and again in the following year, when my husband's father died and his mother came to live with us. But more perhaps than his ministry to me was what this ritual does for Mother as well as for Dad. The impact of this repeated routine of turning toward hospitality and opening their lives to the possibilities of God's healing cannot be analyzed. But I am convinced it has helped them both immeasurably.

This doesn't imply that we no longer endure the times of explosive impatience, that movement toward hostility. An example of this occurred on a visit with my parents in January 1983. Let me share with you the scenario as I recorded it in my journal. It begins with a general description of my observations.

*March 1983* They are both amazingly energetic and vigorous for seventy-two and seventy-four years old. Mom is slowing down noticeably. She sleeps more and her knees get stiff after she sits for a while, but she never complains and good-naturedly tags along with Dad on his compulsive schedule of canoeing, sailing, snorkeling, biking, tennis, and walking. He is indeed amazing.

One day I watched his strong, lean, rapid march to the shore as I helped carry mast and sails behind him. I thought of a length of beef jerky; all substance, no frills. He has a way of giving himself entirely to whatever he is doing. It becomes consuming, the most important thing possible at the time. Because of that deep giving of self and concentration, he gets from each experience a fresh exhilaration and excitement that makes it new and remarkable even though he's done it many times before.

We could probably learn much from that. And perhaps that explains why he has little patience with people who, for lack of anything significant to do or talk about, fill his space with foolish small talk. He can be crude, rude, intolerant of such people, his own family included, but evidently his age bestows on him some freedom to be either irritable or downright insulting when he's faced with such a situation.

At one point I was confronted with an embarrassment I simply had to react to. We had invited an aunt, uncle, and family friend to dinner. I prepared the meal and Dad was on the patio with them when Mother emerged from the trailer in a fresh outfit, smiling her greeting to them. Dad looked up, scowled, and snapped, "Your buttons are buttoned wrong. And you know your shirt is supposed to be tucked in with that skirt!" Mother turned and retreated inside. I was flabbergasted. I went in and soothed her wounded feelings, helped her rebutton and tuck in. She went back out only to hear him growl at one of the others. She started inside again, saying, "It's going to be a long evening."

I sent Mother out, called Dad in, and for the first time in my life, spoke to him as a parent speaks to a child. So no one else could hear, I took him into the bathroom, closed the door, and looked him straight in the eye, saying, "I don't know what's the matter with you, but you are being rude and miserable and these are our guests. We invited them here to dinner. Now get off whatever it is that's bugging you and be kind and courteous to them! Mother hadn't taken one step out there before you insulted her in front of them."

His old face gnarled in an agony of the anger at imperfection that has lived in his gut these many years. "But that outfit isn't made to be worn with the shirt out; I've told her so many times..." "Dad. Dad, what does it matter? It's her *feelings* that matter, not the way she looks. I know you like to have her look nice. She has always taken such care and pride in the way she dresses and looks." A flash of a childhood memory of Mother donning gloves and hat to go shopping jabbed at my own wounded heart. Then I had a sense of his grief and his rage at this cruel thief that so silently yet relentlessly continues to steal her away leaving him absolutely helpless to save her from its insidious destruction. I put my arms around him and in his good ear softly told him, "Dad, you're getting to be like an old lobster; crustier on the outside and more and more sweet and tender on the inside."

With that he smiled and we went back to our guests. He was the perfect host the remainder of the evening. At bedtime, I went in and kissed them both goodnight as they lay in their bed. I turned to go to my room. From out of the dark, I heard his quiet, "Thanks for the nice party."

As I reflect on this incident, I realize the transformation this dreadful disease is causing in each of us, and I'm reminded of Annie Dillard's description of a frog at her beloved Tinker Creek.

At the end of the island I noticed a small green frog. . . . He didn't jump; I crept closer. At last I knelt on the island's winterkilled grass, lost, dumbstruck, staring at the frog in the creek just four feet away. He was a very small frog with wide, dull eyes. And just as I looked at him, he slowly crumpled and began to sag. The spirit vanished from his eyes as if snuffed. His skin emptied and drooped; his very skull seemed to collapse and settle like a kicked tent. He was shrinking before my eyes like a deflating football. I watched the taut, glistening skin on his shoulders ruck, and rumple, and fall. Soon, part of his skin, formless as a pricked balloon, lay in floating folds like bright scum on top of the water: it was a monstrous and terrifying thing. I gaped bewildered, appalled. An oval shadow hung in the water behind the drained frog; then the shadow glided away. The frog skin bag started to sink.

I had read about the giant water bug, but never seen one. . . . Its grasping forelegs are mighty and hooked inward. It seizes a victim with these legs, hugs it tight, and paralyzes it with enzymes injected during a vicious bite. That one bite is the only bite it ever takes. Through the puncture shoot the poisons that dissolve the victim's muscles and bones and organs—all but the skin—and through it the giant water bug sucks out the victim's body, reduced to a juice . . . when the unrecognizable flap of frog skin settled on the creek bottom, swaying, I stood up and brushed the knees of my pants. I couldn't catch my breath.[5]

And so at times I am still breathless with the shock of seeing the work of whatever vicious giant water bug has poisoned Mother's mind, gradually reducing it more and more to a childish perception of things, even affecting the way she responds to light and shadow.

To this day I am startled by unexpected tears that a caring gesture or concerned inquiry about Mother still provokes. In the early days of her illness such a response felt like weakness to me. Now, we are learning a new way of seeing: to love life in its limitations. We are learning to accept this life and death so mingled, so mixed up. Now when I cry, I cry without shame.

# 1 3   ADAPTATION, DETACH-MENT, AND SOLITUDE

I VAGUELY REMEMBER the first few times visiting with my parents when I felt something beyond annoyance or angry impatience with Mother, beyond the anxious concern and bewildered longing for her to be Mom—safe, normal, well, able, happy, all those qualities that allowed me to remain her child. The feeling was impossible to define at the time and it remains difficult to express. It was a dim awareness of some deep, uneasy stirring, a stepping back. I now know it was the beginning of detachment.

Each family member and friend must face the work of detachment, as it is a significant part of our journey. The primary caregiver, however, is most challenged by this task. Recall the trifling incident over Mother's disarranged blouse in the Florida setting. I saw my father in the agonies of determined resistance toward a woman, his wife, no longer able to take care about the way she looked.

The June 1984 paper presented to the Department of Health and Human Services Task Force on Alzheimer's Disease states: "Given the progressive nature of Alzheimer's disease and the progressive adaptation of both individuals (presumably, the afflicted as well as the primary caregiver) and informal caretakers, longitudinal research studies should be encouraged."[1] Indeed. I believe detachment experienced by both the afflicted person and the caregiver is a significant part of such "progressive adaptation." For example, given the same kind of circumstance today, my father would not respond to the situation in such a disagreeable fashion. One rarely hears him indulge in explosive outbursts of temper anymore.

As I scan his letters, I seldom see the words "your mother" or "Dorothy." Rather, I read accounts of taking "Curly-locks" to the hairdresser, being wakened before dawn by "my first mate," or "my mate is napping longer." For several letters after the first serious episode of her wandering from my sister's home in Maine, when local firemen and policemen found her picking flowers several miles up a country road, we heard about "my wildflower picker." When I visit with them, I hear Dad ask, "Well, Mrs. McGillicuddy, are you ready to go for your walk?" All of this is evidence of an evolving detachment Dad has achieved somewhat unconsciously. I believe his diligence in this task may affect the severity of his feelings of loss and have an even greater impact on the length of time he may spend grieving if the day comes that he must place her in a nursing home and be physically detached from her. These changing terms of endearment do not imply that his love for her has diminished. Rather, it acknowledges that she no longer is the woman he knew as wife, lover, or "sweetheart," his favorite soft word for her from their courting days.

As suggested earlier, it is possible to nurture this mutual work of detachment, particularly for the afflicted one, by attending a day-care program for one to five days or for a part of each day weekly. In-home help and absence from home for blocks of time to pursue other interests aids in the detachment process. Placing the afflicted one in a convalescent or nursing home for short periods of time while the caregiver makes a refreshing trip is another way to address seriously the task of detachment for both persons.

I recall a conversation with Mother not long after the doctor diagnosed her illness. As a family, we were unable to discuss her condition openly. Yet invariably when she was alone with me, she spoke candidly: "I don't know why people who have lived full and happy lives can't just die before they become so forgetful that nothing makes any sense any more and we become terrible burdens to the rest of our families." She heaved a heavy sigh.

Hearing my own mother speak of death in this way was not easy. My response was just as uneasy: "Such a future is a fearful thing to think about," I murmured. She remained silent. I had been wrestling with my own demons as I constantly searched literature for opinions about the genetic implications of this disease. I had given much thought to the possibilities and ramifications of suicide should such a curse fall on me.

"I've thought about it a lot, too, Mother. It's a tempting idea to consider the possibility of having some control over the end of your life in the face of such a future. But when it comes right down to it, if you could choose the day to leave this life, when would you decide to go?"

She looked me straight in the eye and with little hesitation said, "To-day. I'm ready right now."

Was this purely a symptom of deep depression over her condition? Or had she already begun her work of detachment? Throughout my growing-up years she had repeated numbers of times the legend of her own mother's demise with senility. In telling the story, was she preparing for the possibility of her own demise with dementia? I wonder.

Can we consciously attend to detachment? I believe we can. In *Spiritual Disciplines for Everyday Living* Ronald Wells writes of the "reciprocating principle of attachment and detachment" throughout our lives. Either voluntarily or involuntarily we detach from homes, friends, jobs, family, and, in turn, open up time and space in our lives for new attachments. "Looking honestly at our lives we discover that involuntary detachment is a frequently recurring fact of our existence. All [such] experiences are within the parentheses of these two ultimate experiences of detachment common to all of us, birth and death." [2]

In the case of a brain-disabled loved one, we are faced with an involuntary detachment we must come to terms with in one way or another. How do we begin? Wells suggests, "We begin by recognizing that even though we [have] no choice, we [are] not destroyed. When we find ourselves intact and even under the necessity of rebuilding our lives, we can experience a new sense of freedom and fearlessness in which reconstruction and new growth can take place." Grateful for the good memories and blessed attachments we felt and can in different ways continue to feel, we can begin to move toward that freedom which asks God what our next attachments are to be, never again "having to be afraid of any future unexpected involuntary detachment which may confront us." [3]

Wells quotes from many of the great spiritual writers, among them Paul Tournier:

When we have received much, we must come some day to the turning point in our destiny when we must let go what we have received, on pain of remaining its prisoner and becoming lost in it...when a person hesitates in my consulting room and is faced with the need to give something up, I understand what it is that is stopping her or him; it is not only an instinctive place which lent...support. It is also a presentiment of that middle-of-the-way anxiety...each one must cross that painful supportless zone [alone].

In these circumstances what can I make my support as I start off once more? What can I use as a thread to guide me forward through the darkness of this moment? I need a sort of radar that would enable me to take off and land blind. That radar, I think, is my conviction that God has a purpose for me, a purpose for each one of us, and at every moment of our lives. I believe that God can lead me, even when I cannot yet see the road clearly in front of me.[4]

Part of my continuing struggle lies in the line, "That radar...is my conviction that God has a purpose for me, a purpose for each one of us and at every moment of our lives." What is Mother's purpose as she becomes more and more dependent and helpless? What is the purpose of your loved one?

"For now we see in a mirror, dimly, but then we will see face to face. Now I know only in part; then I will know fully, even as I have been fully known" (1 Cor. 13:12).[5] Oh, how dimly we see. But glimmers of hope do come into our lives.

Ram Dass expresses this paradox well: "The struggles of those we are helping confront us with life at its purest. Their suffering strips away guile and leaves what is real and essential. The deepest human qualities come forth: openness, yearning, patience, courage, forbearance, faith, humor...living truth...living spirit. Moved and touched by these qualities, we've no choice but to acknowledge and reaffirm our humanity. Others notice when this happens. We feel them feel it. It's at these moments that we remember what service is truly all about."[6]

Although I still battle at times with the demons "why" and "what if," we encounter each other less and less as my focus becomes more engaged with "now" and "how." Perhaps we can experience support in this difficult process of detachment and adaptation if, out of the roots of our religious faith, we are able to see this as a time to learn the difference between loneliness and solitude.

# 1 4   REACHING OUT OF SOLITUDE

"OUR MINDS take their quality from that on which they dwell."[1] This single quote makes a home in my brain and continually returns to remind me of the power inherent in it. Caregiving can be a lonely business. Friends find more interesting, less demanding friendships as they tire of the pain we confront them with by our very existence. When the demands of caregiving deplete our energies, we have little left to give to social occasions, even to reciprocating kindnesses. We can begin to dwell on our loneliness.

Researchers tell us that the pain of loneliness is the most intense, most unbearable kind of suffering a human can encounter; so unbearable that one will go to nearly any length to avoid it.[2]

In our loneliness we tend to keep meticulous accounts of who has visited or phoned, written letters or brought signs of caring through food and favors. "We can't carry on a decent conversation anymore. It's like being trapped here with a two-year-old all day and all night," we complain. And if honesty is possible we might add, "I can't stand it any longer. I've got to get out of here. It's either her or me." Usually we avoid such honesty. It's our friends who shake their heads and mutter, "I don't know how he stands it any longer."

It is true. We must find ways to get away. But we also need to develop the habit of a silent attentiveness to the strength that lies deep within. We must try to find that calm center at the very eye of the storm that buffets us. That calm center can become a home for us. Perhaps that's the place Brian Wren was writing from:

*Dear Mother God, you held me at my birth*
*You sang my name, were glad to see my face*
*You are my sky, my shining sun*
*and in your love there's always room to be and grow*
*to find a home, a settled place.*[3]

The habit of dwelling in this quiet, settled place does not come easily, nor does it come without practice. Nothing worthwhile does. But when we begin to draw strength from this mysterious interior source, we cease to keep accounts and begin to respond with joy, receiving others as they come to us. We find ourselves losing interest in judging other people and interpreting their actions. Conflict and worry don't hang around as much anymore. They are replaced by sometimes overwhelming feelings of appreciation and even periods of deep contentment, especially when contemplating the beauty of nature. Smiles come to our lips more often and we begin to embrace the attitude of letting things happen rather than trying to make things happen by our dictate. But most of all we become deeply sensitive to the love extended by others and our own need to extend it.[4]

Loneliness can move us between two extremes. We may withdraw from the company of others only to emerge incessantly chattering, as though we had not engaged in conversation for months. Or, we may work at a frenzied schedule of activities that keeps us occupied so fully we have no time to think. Either extreme fails to honor the growth of the spirit possible in solitude.

I meet regularly with a group of women who live in a nearby retirement complex. All of them are of advanced age and have passed through that time of decision making and loss (detachment), giving up their homes to become one of hundreds in this comfortable institution. All who were married have lost their mates. Frequently we discuss the differences between loneliness and solitude.

One woman had recently passed through a difficult illness. She spoke of waking one night with the awesome awareness of being alone. "I realized there was no one I could call on or rely on. There was no one but me and God. But he was there, he is always there."

Another woman listened carefully to several examples of the struggle in moving from loneliness to solitude. Finally she spoke. "Having never married, I learned long ago how to be alone. The value of solitude has continued to serve me, especially now as I have more and more difficulty hearing."

"When I find myself craving the presence of others, I know that is loneliness," spoke another. "Solitude brings a sense of satisfaction, comfort with my own thoughts and feelings. Loneliness is feeling sorry for myself. It is negative, passive, restless. Solitude leads to growth and activity, but is restful."

To become comfortable with one's inner voice, to allow time to listen to that which rises from within, prepares us for beauty seldom before heard or seen. This inner alertness is like the musician who tunes the instrument by listening carefully and adjusting it minutely before beginning to play. We can continue the analogy as we recognize the discipline required in practicing this rarely discussed way of living.

Let's return to the sentence referred to earlier, from my journal: "I had a sense of his grief... his rage at this cruel thief that... continues to steal her away, leaving him absolutely helpless to save her from its insidious destruction." I was wrong. Here is a man who finds helplessness so intolerable a condition that it is unthinkable. Slowly, painfully, he has adapted. He has learned to shelter himself and to find strength in his faith. Remaining on the job as full-time caregiver with very little outside help, he finds his recreation and escape through reading and study of business magazines, stockholders' reports, newspapers, and an extremely lively and varied mail correspondence. He keeps up a regular communication with each of his ten grandchildren.

Not all of us are fashioned this way. Some of us need depression wrung from despair to protect ourselves from death. As caregivers we can watch that frog only so long, then we must avert our eyes and move along life's path without having to confront hourly the slow, agonizing, monstrous death we know is happening. We cast about for help from family, doctors, friends, agencies, and institutions. And it is good to do so. As a people we must continue to work for the improvement of such agencies, services, and institutions so that they will be strong and able to meet our needs.

For each person, circumstances and strength to respond differ. We can become overwhelmed by a sense of powerlessness over the realities brought to us each day through the media: terrorist attacks, starving thousands in Africa, brutal murders in families, wars, and secret government involvements. So, too, this same powerlessness can overwhelm and crush us in our daily slavery to the outrageous task we face as care-givers. For we do, indeed, become slaves. Ultimately, as long as we keep our loved one at home, we must choose between resentment or accep-tance of that fact.

One caregiver who accomplished this task of acceptance spoke with simple vigor: "I can make a difference in the quality of her life because she responds to my presence. You either have to get strong or you get weak. I don't quit living."

"Life is difficult."[5] Those with the will to accept this (and the accept-ing is far from simple) and to meet head-on the difficulties they face, are not left absolutely helpless in any circumstances where there is still life. Strengthened by our faith and by our community of friends, we can be receptive to the smallest generosities of life, however they come.

This quote from a letter my father wrote to our daughter in nurse's training years ago indicates his grasp of this concept: "Your comments re. schoolwork and how much you really like it, even though it is tough, make me very happy. I'm glad it is tough. So is life, and one cannot hope to excel without tough training!" Further on he wrote, "You spoke about the travel you dream about in years to come, and I'm sure those dreams will come true. We do not know what lies around the corner but I recall the words of a very wise person: 'The life that shall flourish is the life that adapts to its environment.'"

A neighbor ran in one day while my parents were visiting. She had just seen Mother walking alone several blocks from the house. Was she all right? Fearful of the approaching night and wooded areas nearby, I drove around looking for her, my heart pounding. When I found her and told her who I was, she got in the car. I wrapped my arms around her. "Were you lost?"

"I guess so."

"Were you afraid?"

"No, not really. I didn't mean..." And then she startled me by repeating nearly word for word the statement she'd spoken five years be-fore: "I don't know why, when people get so they can't remember any-thing, they can't just die."

This time my response was different. "Mother, we all grow old in different ways. Some people lose their sight and can never again see the beauty we've been enjoying this fall season. Some become crippled and can never take a walk like you and Dad do every day." She listened in-tently, trying hard to hold on to the words. "Others, like Dad, begin to lose their hearing. It's hard to grow old and face these losses. But think of the things we can still enjoy together."

She brightened. "Yes, that's true." It was a moment of communion in which we touched a part of each other that had never changed. Her courage in adapting, in continuing to try, to live patiently, to face bravely the growing unknown, challenges me in my own journey.

To be blessed is to be present to the gentleness I witnessed most recently sitting with them at their small table. Mother tried to express something without success. Shaking her head she said, "I...can't... connect anything." Dad reached out his hands and took both of hers. "There, now," he soothed. "We're connected."

Although she no longer knows who he is or who she is and is losing her ability to speak a complete thought, she is happiest now when he is near her. Yet we know that the day of separation approaches. When she no longer recognizes or responds to his presence and he is unable to care for her in their home, they will be parted.

My astonishment grows as I observe my father. His difficulties are compounded by a progressive loss of hearing, yet he tells about little repair jobs he's done for others, food he prepared for a sick neighbor, his offers to "keep an eye on things and to water the shrubs," the assurance to a new neighbor, a working widow, that "if there's anything I can do for you, I hope you'll let me know."

Repairing a clock, rebuilding the roof of the bird feeder, building himself a small toolbox may seem inconsequential to many, but these are the things he contents himself with. All the while Mother sits or paces nearby. Sometimes an easy patter passes between them full of repeated responses; sometimes a comfortable silence falls upon them. Dad talks to her occasionally at great length; he ignores the fact that she doesn't understand or respond. Nothing is too ridiculous to cheer him. One day I heard him singing an old nursery rhyme to her while he worked: "Sing a song of sixpence, a pocketful of rye...."

By accepting faithfully, by living with a view toward the hospitable end of life, receptively open to others, comfortable in and fed by our solitude, we find courage. It's a paradox: we find ourselves able to reach out, yes, even to serve others while living the daily, hourly difficulty of companionship with one who is increasingly brain damaged. We can do it, by God's grace, because the afflicted one is a loved and cared-for person.

## POEMS

### DUET (EXCERPT)

*Water trickles through a quiet wooded den*
*where skunk cabbages are first to rise in spring*
*along banks melting into ooze and pebbles*
*reflecting shards of sun. If you listen*
*let the silence run a cycle through your veins*
*you can hear it sing its quiet murmuring*
*a skein of healing yarn, a thread embroidering*
*the edges of a torn and ragged time.*
          —Martha O. Adams, 1995

### MOTHER

*Raw*
*wounded*
*don't touch me*
*don't even speak her name*
*lest you cause unbidden tears*
*that aggravate my shame.*

*Sparkling*
*laughing*
*she lived*
*drinking life deeply*
*nourishing family and friends.*
*Together they shared joy, sorrow...*
*now it is he who tends.*

*Puzzled*
*struggling*
*she lives*
*a question mark*
*her perpetual mask*
*trying with courage to understand*
*hesitant; fearful to ask.*

*Wisdom*
*courage*
*we seek.*
*Guide us, Friend,*
*on this path untrod*
*as we help her journey*
*toward the arms of God.*

*Raw*
*wounded*
*please touch me.*
*Speak loud her name.*
*You may cause unbidden tears...*
*I am done with shame.*
                    —Martha O. Adams, 1979

## I HEAR THE SIGHTS OF THINGS

(Written soon after we put the house up for sale prior to my parents'
move to Florida.)

*At three A.M. like Scrooge's ghost*
*it came and yanked me back*
*through stricken house alone*
*remembering my child self*

*at the foot of towering clock*
*transfixed by ticking pendulum*
*wondering*
*where is the grandfather?*

*The silver cup*
*cold on my cheek*
*empties clacking train sounds*
*in my ear.*
*Young Dorothy from Kansas*
*pampered in white dress*
*spills dusty landscape down the front*
*all the way to Niobe, New York.*

*Her mother nods*
*dreaming*
*of dashing young husband*
*hot and heavy horsed*
*pounding his way home from Dodge City*
*the tall glass vase saddle-hitched*
*flecked with foam and sod*
*brilliant blue consolation*

*the lonely bride waits*
*carelessly filling*
*brownsugarstained*
*blue willowware*
*her mother used*
*to civilize*
*to dignify*
*at tea*
*in the one room soddy*
*in the side of the draw.*
—Martha Ellen Olds Adams Rucker Mather Parrott,
daughter of Dorothy, granddaughter of Edith and
Ellen, 1983

## SIMPLIFYING

*Pleading the silent question*
*her eyes dart from face to face*
*an aging wounded bird*
*crumpled into the corner of the couch.*

*Her eyes dart from face to face*
*"The house has to be sold, Mother."*
*crumpled into the corner of the couch*
*Why? Why? Why?*

*"The house has to be sold, Mother."*
*Father and daughter resume*
*Why? Why? Why?*
*scheming their intricate plot.*

*Father and daughter resume*
*spinning cobwebs of despair*
*scheming their intricate plot*
*(How do birds die, Mommy?)*

*Spinning cobwebs of despair*
*Who is she? Where are we?*
*(How do birds die, Mommy?)*
*"What about my rugs?"*

*Who is she? Where are we?*
*Her feathers ruffle in agitation*
*"What about my rugs?"*
*"We'll bring a few of the little ones."*

*An aging wounded bird*
*stranded between home and Home*
*pleading the silent question*
*(Where does Jesus live, Mommy?)*
—Martha O. Adams, 1983

## TO BELIEVE

*To believe in God is to celebrate*
*the gift of life in the presence of death.*
*It is easy to celebrate life on the good days*
*when the sun is shining and laughter floats*
*through the air and children play and lovers love.*

*But life is more than sunshine.*
*There is also dusk and the starless night*
*when laughter dies and fear clings to the soul…*
*fear of losing someone dear.*

*That's when celebration becomes an act of faith.*
*Not a soft faith full of heavenly promises, or a*
*bromide faith which dulls the sharp throb of grief,*
*but an open faith… open to the dawn and to the dark.*
*A faith that reaches up to claim life's highest joys*
*and kneels down to taste the bitter wine of failure*
*and disappointment and sadness.*
*A faith that seeks every mood and in that exposure*
*grows more sensitive feels more pain*
*knows more joy.*

*To believe in God is to celebrate life.*
*Not a piece of life but all of it*
*the good and the bad, the happy and the sad.*
*Because God gave it all*
*and we live when we receive it all*
*and love it and use it and live it.*

*To believe in God is not to deny*
*the presence of ugliness*
*but to transform it into beauty;*
*not to deny the sounds of discord*
*but to blend them into harmony;*
*not to deny the confusion of chaos*
*but to create order.*

*To believe in God is to take anger*
*and make it into a sensitizing of the soul;*
*to take hatred*
*and transform it into a ministry of love.*
*To believe in God is to take the broken pieces of life*
*and fashion them into a cross.*
                                    —Rev. Wilbur Daniels

## KEEP THE CANDLES LIT

(This poem about the last days of my dear friend Clair Seymour is dedicated to my father, another lighter of candles.)

*Clair is on her way out.*
*I keep the candles lit for her departure*
*flames of poems*
*brilliant skies*
*"God's air"*
*flashing prose*
*letters shared*
*quivering memories explored*
*soap bubbles on the wind.*

*Daily she floats*
*lighter, paler*
*wistful translucence indrawn*
*like breath preparing for the ride*
*within the bubbles on the wind.*
*"How good to fly into the air*
*and dance away," she says*
*blowing through the plastic ring.*
*"I feel the Spirit has left me," she sighs.*
*The candles dim for her*
*flickering brightly.*

*I think of how exuberantly*
*we light the candles for the coming in.*
*Great expectations kindle flames of joy*
*announced in gay and gifting showers*
*cribberies, teddy bears and Mother Goose.*
*How well we keep the candles lit*
*until that day when they can handle*
*matches safely on their own*
*and we begin to search for ways*
*to keep our own fires warm.*

*From whence does that impatient energy arise?*
*What source is left depleted by a mother's agony?*
*Ripening cells dividing in a frenzy*
*to accomplish that first gasp of light.*
*Oh, we want the candles lit*
*for that first unfocused sight.*
*We strike the fire without a thought*
*for unknown Source of life bereft*
*of this its own precious*
*breath of potentiality.*

*Clair is on her way.*
*I keep the candles lit for her departure*
*flames of poems*
*brilliant skies*
*"God's air"*
*flashing prose*
*letters shared*
*quivering memories explored*
*soap bubbles on the wind.*

*Daily she floats*
*lighter, paler*
*wistful translucence indrawn*
*breath preparing for the ride*
*within the bubbles on the wind.*
*"How good to fly into the air*
*and dance away," she says*
*watching as I blow into the ring.*

*"I feel the Spirit has left me," she sighs.*
*I strike the match*
*and light the candle one more time.*
*"The Spirit is gathering you in."*
*It is I who feel the spirit leaving.*
*The candles dim for her*
*flickering brightly.*
                    —Martha O. Adams, 1986

## SONNET 2 FROM "THE AUTUMN SONNETS"

*If I can let you go as trees let go*
*Their leaves, so casually, one by one;*
*If I can come to know what they do know,*
*That fall is the release, the consummation,*
*Then fear of time and the uncertain fruit*
*Would not distemper the great lucid skies*
*This strangest autumn, mellow and acute.*
*If I can take the dark with open eyes*
*And call it seasonal, not harsh or strange*
*(For love itself may need a time of sleep),*
*And, treelike, stand unmoved before the change,*
*Lose what I lose to keep what I can keep,*
*The strong root still alive under the snow,*
*Love will endure—if I can let you go.*[1]
                    —May Sarton

## ESTABLISHING THE LINE (EXCERPT)

*Not until her mother flew away*
*to freedom    in the thin air . . .*
*pausing that afternoon*
*down by the lake*
*for one last feast of faces    hers,*
*hovered over the curling waves*
*humming with blue dragonflies,*
*stitched the lonely pair*
*with long darts of joy    memories*
*some memories she took with her*
*in a bulging envelope clasped*
*beneath her wing    still sealed*
*and marked "return to sender"*
*. . . that's when it all began.*

*. . . Now that her mother's gone*
*she takes her hungering to bed*
*and sometimes rises knowing she's been fed*
*yet hungering. She gazes down*

*the long dark tunnel*
*red lights on the last car*
*of the last subway train fading*
*out of sight    and wonders*
*how she will get around    move*
*from here to there alone without*
*the warm tone of reassuring sounds*
*that mothers make    her skill*
*in mending things    creating something new*
*from that old box of fabrics on the basement shelf*

*her love of dancing    her hospitality    generosity*
*the hundreds of loaves of warm baked bread*
*and soups and casseroles with*
*herbs and spices from around the globe*
*stirred deep and simmered with the bones*
*delivered unannounced where there was need*
*or tucked away for grubby    bent*
*unshaven men who unexpectedly*
*appeared at the back door. Some*
*people called them bums*
*and were afraid of them. She*
*said it was the war that made*
*the people grey and poor.*

*And then the questions begin to rise...*
*her mother (familiar with the way*
*of yeast    the temperature must be just right*
*a little sweetening helps it all to grow)*
*safely tucked beyond the skies*
*could she be listening?*
                —Martha O. Adams, 1995

## GOD OF THE OPEN AIR (EXCERPT)

(I found reference to this poem hastily scrawled in Mother's handwriting across the front of an old church bulletin. This segment from the poem "God of the Open Air," probably read in church, speaks eloquently for Mother and the way she lived.)

*These are the things I prize*
*And hold of dearest worth*
*Light of the sapphire skies,*
*Peace of the silent hills*
*Shelter of the forests, comfort of the grass,*
*Music of birds, murmurs of little rills,*
*Shadows of cloud that swiftly pass,*
*And, after showers,*
*The smell of flowers*
*And of the good brown earth.*
*And best of all, along the way, friendship and mirth.*

*These are the gifts I ask*
*Of Thee, Spirit serene;*
*Strength for the daily task,*
*Courage to face the road,*
*Good cheer to help me bear the traveler's load,*
*And, for the hours of rest that come between,*
*An inward joy of all things heard and seen.*
*These are the sins I fain*
*Would have Thee take away;*
*Malice and cold disdain,*
*Hot anger, sullen hate,*
*Scorn of the lowly, envy of the great,*
*And discontent that casts a shadow gray*
*On all the brightness of the common day.*[2]
    —Henry Van Dyke, from *Arbor Day*

I recently came across a letter from Mother written to me in 1954, on the night before I was to leave for Berlin as an exchange student. This poem, whose title and author I do not know, connects me in deep ways with Mother and her mother, Ellen, after whom I was named. She writes: "Here is a little poem my mother gave me I think you will like."

*I cannot tell why there should come to me*
*A thought of someone miles and miles away*
*In swift insistence on the memory*
*Unless there be a need that I should pray.*

*Perhaps just then my child has fiercer fight,*
*A more appalling weakness or decay*
*Of courage; darkness, some lost sense of right;*
*And so, in case you need my prayer, I pray.*

*Dear, do the same for me; if I intrude*
*Unasked upon you, on some crowded day.*
*Give me a moment's prayer as interlude;*
*Be very sure I need it, therefore pray.*

# NOTES

## FOREWORD

1. Author's note: From "The New Wrinkles of an Aging World," *New York Times,* September 22, 1996: "Some 22 million people around the world are believed to have Alzheimer's and other forms of dementia. The number is soaring with the aging of the population, for in the 1990's alone, the number of people over age 65 in the world is set to rise by 30%. American gerontologist, Dr. Robert N. Butler, wrote in a recently published academic paper: 'We will be confronted with the disease of the 20th century being transformed into the epidemic of the 21st.'"

## PROLOGUE:
## CONVERSATIONS WITH A PRIMARY CAREGIVER

1. Ronald V. Wells, *Spiritual Disciplines for Everyday Living* (Bridgeport, Conn.: R.D.C. Books, 1982; 4th printing, 1998). Ronald Wells can be contacted at 3030 Park, Bridgeport, CT 06604.
2. Elizabeth Gray Vining, *A Quest There Is,* Pendle Hill Pamphlet no. 246 (Wallingford, Pa.: Pendle Hill Publications, 1982), 23.

## 1. BEGINNINGS

1. Marsha Fretwell, M.D., "Alzheimer's: A Very Human Problem," *Signs and Symptoms* 11, no. 1 (fall 1985): 4–5.
2. Lisa Gwyther, "Risk Factors and Alzheimer's Disease," paper published by the Joseph and Kathleen Bryan Alzheimer's Disease Research Center, Education and Information Research Training Core, Duke University Medical Center, May 1997.

## 2. Legal Issues

1. Public Law 98-459, October 9, 1984, 98th Cong. An act to extend the authorization of appropriations for, and to revise, the Older American Act of 1965. Cited as the "Older Americans Act Amendments of 1984."

2. *Public Policy Update,* November 1997, Alzheimer's Association Washington Public Policy Office, Washington, D.C. For more information write Susan Goldenson, Editor, 1319 F St., NW, Suite 710, Washington, D.C. 20004, or e-mail her at Susan.Goldenson@alz.org.

3. Carrie Tuhy, "When an Aging Parent Needs Financial Help," *Money* 12, no. 9 (September 1983): 93–98.

4. L. Daniel Akers Jr. of Merrill Lynch, Hendersonville, North Carolina, is the certified financial planner I consulted on the revocable living trust in June 1998. The following advice on financial planning is given by Akers. Please consult your own financial planner for specific advice.

5. Don McLeod, "Home-Care Patients Feel Unfairly Targeted," *AARP Bulletin* 39, no. 4 (April 1998).

6. Carol A. Schwab, a member of the North Carolina State Bar and a Family Resource Management Specialist for the NC Cooperative Extension Service, North Carolina State University, publishers of *Medicaid Eligibility for Nursing Home Care: A Guide for North Carolinians,* issued as publication FCS-420, May 1997.

7. 42 CRF 1005; 409.904. F.S., Florida Medicaid Institutional Care Program Eligibility, 1996.

8. Michael Gilfix, "Legal Strategies for Patient and Family," *Generations* 9, no. 2 (winter 1984): 46–48.

9. Ellice Fatoullah and David E. Fraser, "Ask the Lawyer," *ADRDA Newsletter* 5, no. 2 (summer 1985), 10.

10. Agency for Health Care Administration, *Florida Medicaid Summary of Services,* July 1995, p. 29.

11. From a telephone conversation March 8, 1986, with Mary Clarkson, Office of Management and Budget, Health Care Finance Administration, Washington, D.C.

12. "Check Your Patient's Life Insurance," *ADRDA Newsletter,* August– September 1984.

13. The following sources were used as the basis for this chapter, along with those already cited. Robert N. Brown, *The Rights of Older Persons* (New York: Avon Books, 1979); Dale R. Deteifs, *1985 Guide to Social Security* (n.p.: William M. Mercer-Meidinger, 1985); Congressman Stewart B.

McKinney, comp., *Handbook for Older Americans*, compiled for residents of Connecticut's Fourth District; *Families, Informal Supports and Alzheimer's Disease: Current Research and Future Needs*, prepared as a working document by the Work Group on Families, Informal Supports, and Alzheimer's Disease of the Department of Health and Human Services Task Force on Alzheimer's Disease; *Connecticut Elder Law: A Desktop Manual*, 1995, Elder Law Section of the Connecticut Bar Association; James L. Dam, "Lawyers Threatened by Medicaid Law," *Lawyers Weekly USA*, September 8, 1997.

## 3. PROGRESSIVE STAGES

1. Medicine, *Newsweek*, December 3, 1984, 56–62.
2. Marilyn Pajk, "Alzheimer's Disease Inpatient Care," *American Journal of Nursing* 84, no. 2 (February 1984): 217. The specific information about the duration of the disease is taken from a footnote in this article attributed to D. Terry and P. Davies, "Dementia of the Alzheimer's Type," *Annual Review of Neuroscience* 3 (1980): 77–95.
3. Benson Schaeffer, "The Psychologist's Corner," *Portland Newsletter for ADRDA*, August 19, 1983, 4.
4. Robert Merrill Eddy and Kathy Wonson Eddy, *Writing with Light*, (Cleveland: United Church Press, 1997), 36. This beautiful book is a visual feast filled with profound and spirit-lifting insights. Kathy Eddy's writings are short and provocative enough to be shared together with your loved one who suffers AD. The photographs will stir pleasant memories that could focus your day together in a positive way. If you have a piano and are fortunate enough to read music, the simple songs and hymns sprinkled throughout minister to deep needs so often unexpressed, and can help make long days endurable.
5. Kathy Higley, "Caregiver Tip: Touching Is Not Taboo," *St. Louis ADRDA Newsletter*, May 1984, 4.

## 4. MAINTAINING COMMUNICATION

1. This observation was made in a lecture given by Dr. Barry Reisberg. At the time of the lecture, Dr. Reisberg was senior research psychiatrist and clinical director of the Geriatric Study and Treatment Program at New York University Medical Center. He has written *A Guide to Alzheimer's Disease: For Families, Spouses and Friends* (New York: Free Press, 1984), and edited *Alzheimer's Disease: The Standard Reference Book* (New York: Free Press, 1983).

## 6. SEXUAL AND EMOTIONAL NEEDS

1. This subject is addressed seriously and with sensitivity by Donna Cohen and Carl Eisdorfer in their outstanding book *The Loss of Self: A Family Resource for the Care of Alzheimer's Disease and Related Disorders* (New York: W. W. Norton & Co., 1986), chap. 6. *Sexuality and Alzheimer's Disease*, publication no. X-22, a two-part bibliography compiled by the National Institute on Aging's Rush Alzheimer Disease Center at the Rush Presbyterian-St. Luke's Medical Center, Chicago, Illinois. A free copy may be ordered by calling the ADEAR Center at 800-438-4380.

2. This material is drawn in part from Marilyn Pajk, "Alzheimer's Disease Inpatient Care," *American Journal of Nursing* 84, no. 2 (February 1984): 216–32.

3. Two excellent resources with action steps for specific ways to respond to the feelings and needs of the AD patient: a 1992 flyer entitled "Feelings" and a two-page piece entitled "Suggestions for the Alzheimer's Caregiver and Patient," both available from the Alzheimer's Association by calling 800-272-3900.

## 7. ADVANCED STAGES

1. This subject also is covered well by Donna Cohen and Carl Eisdorfer, *The Loss of Self,* chap. 5.

2. Information about drug therapy comes from the *ADRDA Newsletter* 2, no. 1 (January 1984).

3. This came from the 1995 booklet by Caroline McNeil, "Alzheimer's Disease: Unraveling the Mystery," publication no. 95-3782, Public Information Office, National Institute on Aging/National Institutes of Health.

4. Ibid. The National Institute on Aging, one of the National Institutes of Health, leads the federal effort on AD and aging research on the epidemiology, cause, diagnosis, and management of AD. Write NIA, Building 31, Room 5C-27, Bethesda, MD 20892; or call 301-496-1752.

5. Stanley M. Aronson, M.D., "Alzheimer's: The Gray Plague," *Signs and Symptoms* 11, no. 1 (fall 1985): 8–9.

6. Several excellent resources for caregivers are available: Jo-Ann Friedman, *Home Health Care: A Complete Guide for Patients and Their Families* (New York: W. W. Norton & Co., 1986); Alzheimer's Association, *The Family Guide for Alzheimer's Care in Residential Settings* (Alzheimer's Association, 1992); and Lisa Gwyther, *Home Is Where I Remember Things: A Curriculum for Home and Community Alzheimer's Care,* available from Duke Fam-

ily Support Program, Box 3600, Duke University Medical Center, Durham, NC 27710 ($15).

7. This unofficial study by Walter E. Lobo is based on a questionnaire answered by forty-four members of four AD support groups. Prepared in March 1985, the scope of the questionnaire and summary is quite complete, addressing such problems as sleeping, eating, use of medication, bathing, dressing, and confusion. For more references on care of the incontinent person, see "Helpful Resources" section.

8. For information on continence problems, write to the National Association for Continence (NAFC), P.O. Box 8310, Spartanburg, SC 29305, and request their newsletter "Quality Care." For a catalog of home health care items from AARP, write AARP Pharmacy Service, P.O. Box 13671, Richmond, VA 23286-2616, or call 800-456-2277. Sears also publishes a catalog of home health care products.

9. This recipe for bowel regulation was passed along to me by a caregiver who picked it up from a health care professional. Her loved one enjoys using it on his breakfast toast. It has made "all the difference" for both of them.

Fruited Paste
1 lb. pitted prunes
1 c. lemon juice
1 c. brown sugar
1 lb. raisins
1 lb. dried figs
1 package Senna Tea (3- or 4-oz. package) (usually found in health food stores)
Steep the tea for five minutes in 3½ cups boiling water. Strain. Cut the fruit into small pieces. To 2 cups of tea, add the fruit and boil for 5 minutes. Add sugar and lemon juice. Cool mixture. Process until smooth in blender or food processor. When blended, place mixture in small plastic containers and freeze. Take 1 or 2 tablespoons daily.

10. Deodorizing cleanser sprays and lotions are listed in the catalogs mentioned in note 8. They are also available in pharmacies that handle health aids for disabled persons.

11. Marshelle Thobaben and Linda Anderson, "Reporting Elder Abuse: It's the Law," *American Journal of Nursing* 85 (April 1985): 371–74.

## 8. Support Services

1. See also, *Staying at Home: A Guide to Long-Term Care and Housing* (Washington, D.C.: American Association of Retired Persons, 1996). This is a resource rich in information, with addresses and phone numbers of vital organizations and institutions, home health sources, meal services, directories, how-to booklets, and the many options for the needs of retired people.

2. "Private Long Term Care Insurance: To Buy or Not to Buy," *Special Report 34,* 1995, United Seniors Health Cooperative, 1331 H St., NW, Suite 500, Washington, DC 20005-4706.

3. Ibid.

4. "Part III: Administrative, Procedural, and Miscellaneous," Long Term Care Services and Insurance, notice 97-31, 213, 7702B, and 4980C of the Internal Revenue Code.

5. *The Caregiver: Newsletter of the Duke Family Support Program* 16, no. 3 (fall 1996): 19.

## 9. Choosing a Nursing Home

1. Juliette Warshauer, "Helpful Hints on When to Place in a Nursing Home," *ADRDA Newsletter* 3, no. 1 (spring 1983): 6.

2. These questions were compiled and this section completed after study of the following publications: *Families Who Care for Older Relatives: The Problems, the Solutions,* Connecticut Community Care, Inc., with support from Blue Cross and Blue Shield of Connecticut, Inc.; *When Care Is Needed,* published in 1983 by the Connecticut State Department on Aging, 80 Washington Street, Hartford, CT 06106; *How to Select a Nursing Home,* published in 1984 by the Illinois Department of Public Health, Office of Health Regulations, 525 West Jefferson Street, Springfield, IL 62761; *Thinking About a Nursing Home?* published by the American Health Care Association, 1200 15th Street, N.W., Washington, DC 20005; R. Barker Bausell and Michael A. Rooney, *Nursing Homes: How to Evaluate and Select a Nursing Home* (Emmaus, Pa.: People's Medical Society, 1983); "Planning for the Elderly: Nursing Home Checklist," *Publication 289,* Matthew Bender & Co., Rel. 18, January 1995; Michael J. McCann, "Know Where You Are Going and What to Expect When You Get There: Understanding Long-Term Care Facility Options," *Elder Law: The Newsletter of the NCBA's Elder Law Section* 2 (April 1998).

3. Mary Adelaide Mendelson, *Tender Loving Greed* (New York: Random House, 1975), 9. This exposé of nursing home scandal and fraud was suggested as a resource by the director of the Fairfield, Connecticut, Department on Aging. I hope we have come a long way since 1975 in improving care for our aged, but disturbing stories of institutional abuse and fraud continue to make the news.

4. Ibid., 9.

5. Robert Langreth, "After Seeing Profits from the Poor, Some HMOs Abandon Them," *Wall Street Journal,* April 7, 1998.

6. Michael Moss and Chris Adams, "For Medicaid Patients, Doors Slam Closed," *Wall Street Journal,* April 7, 1998.

7. *Tender Loving Greed,* 179.

8. Thanks to an agreement in 1998 between Mission Hospital and the Asheville, North Carolina, Alzheimer's Association, the cost to the family for a brain autopsy done for Alzheimer's research purposes is $250. This covers the cost of removing the brain tissue locally and sending it to Boston, where the autopsy and research are underwritten by other sources. Contact your local Alzheimer's Association office for information.

9. June White and Leonard L. Heston, M.D., *Dementia: A Practical Guide to Alzheimer's Disease and Related Illnesses* (New York: W. H. Freeman Co., 1983). For more information on autopsies, see *Pathologist* 40, no. 6 (June 1986).

## 10. A GROWING SERENITY

1. Wells, *Spiritual Disciplines for Everyday Living,* 152, 153, 155. Wells quotes from page 28 of Elizabeth Gray Vining's *The World in Tune* (Wallingford, Pa.: Pendle Hill Publications, 1968): "I am thinking of what I have learned to call minor ecstasies, bits of star dust which are for all of us, however monotonous our days and cramped our lives, however limited our opportunities...that fleeting instant when we lose ourselves in joy and wonder...minor because it is slight and so soon gone...an ecstasy because there is an impersonal quality in the vivid thrust of happiness we feel, and because the stir lingers in the memory. Fragments of beauty and truth lie in every path; they need only the seeing eye and the receptive spirit."

Wells writes: "To have the joy of a lifted heart is to cultivate a lifestyle in which our directed attention is sensitive to all that is good and true and beautiful. Then we begin to expand our awareness of joy in our actual living experience; we become free, open, warm-hearted and radiant...resolving to live sensitively and unhurriedly so that we will be prepared to receive and appreciate these minor ecstasies as they enter our lives. Once we have entered into this discipline, it is truly remarkable how many of them break in upon us in the course of a routine week."

2. This reference is to a famous character from Fyodor Dostoyevsky's *Brothers Karamazov*. The Grand Inquisitor interrogates Christ, who has returned to earth again. The encounter is a classic discussion of the meaning of good, evil, and suffering.

3. The Jewish understanding of the broader word, "shalom," implies this same idea of perfection as completeness, unity, wholeness, justice, peace, hello, good-bye. In the Genesis Creation story, all is declared good by God except man and woman. Jewish commentary understands this to mean that humans are incomplete at Creation, lacking the striving toward God through which humans become complete. It is also believed that in the face of disaster, God sends a child rather than a miracle to help make the world complete, thereby making human beings partners with God in the continuation of Creation.

4. This thinking was stimulated by John Sanford's *Evil, the Shadow Side of Reality* (New York: Crossroad, 1981). This is his definition of "persona."

## 11. RELIEF THROUGH HUMOR

1. M. Scott Peck, M.D., *The Road Less Traveled* (New York: Simon & Schuster, 1978), 69–70.

2. M. Scott Peck, M.D., *People of the Lie* (New York: Simon & Schuster, 1983), 222.

3. Marshall Cheney, director of Patient and Family Services, from "Keeping Depression at the Door," *The Caregiver: Newsletter of the Duke Family Support Program* 17, no. 1 (spring 1997).

## 12. A CALL TO SAINTHOOD

1. Dietrich Bonhoeffer, excerpt from *Letters and Papers from Prison* (New York: Simon & Schuster, 1971), 215–17. In his long and deeply moving poem, Bonhoeffer evokes exquisitely his feelings about the last visit of his fiancée, Maria, and the agony of her retreating footsteps.

2. Ibid., 156, 167, 168, 176, 177, 190.

3. Henri J. M. Nouwen, *Reaching Out* (Garden City, N.Y.: Doubleday & Co., 1975).

4. Nicholas Sparks, *The Notebook* (New York: Warner Books, 1996).

5. Annie Dillard, *Pilgrim at Tinker Creek* (New York: Harper & Row, 1974), 6–7.

## 13. ADAPTATION, DETACHMENT, AND SOLITUDE

1. From *Families, Informal Supports, and Alzheimer's Disease: Current Research and Future Needs*, prepared as a working document by the Work Group on Families, Informal Supports, and Alzheimer's Disease of the Department of Health and Human Services Task Force on Alzheimer's Disease, Washington, D.C., 1984.

2. Wells, *Spiritual Disciplines for Everyday Living*, 128, 129.

3. Ibid., 129, 130.

4. Ibid., 135.

5. This passage from St. Paul is often quoted without its powerfully satisfying and instructive conclusion: "even as I have been fully known." For both the AD sufferer and caregiver, who know that no other person can fully understand his or her suffering and the tumult and depression it can bring, this acknowledgment that we are fully understood by God is most comforting. Our instruction comes in the following verse: "And now faith, hope, and love abide, these three; and the greatest of these is love" (1 Cor. 13:13).

6. Ram Dass and Paul Gorman, *How Can I Help?* (New York: Alfred A. Knopf, 1985), 142.

## 14. REACHING OUT OF SOLITUDE

1. M. V. Dunlop, *Stillness and Strength and Contemplative Meditation* (Chatham, Eng.: Parrett and Neves, Ltd., 1933), 14.

2. In Maggie Scarf's comprehensive volume, *Unfinished Business: Pressure Points in the Lives of Women* (Garden City, N.Y.: Doubleday & Co., 1980), she tells of her surprise in discovering the desperate and unendurable quality of loneliness experienced by many women. This loneliness ultimately sends them out to establish contact in spite of their defeating life circumstances.

3. This is the first verse of the song by the Reverend Dr. Brian A. Wren, "Dear Mother God," from the collection *Faith Renewed* (Carol Stream, Ill.: Hope Publishing, 1995). Had I known this lovely song I would have sung it to Mother when she was searching so desperately for "home."

4. Some of these thoughts were found in Alice C. Soder's *Faith Walk: A Newsletter for Seekers* 3, no. 3 (May 1998). This newsletter is published by FaithWorks Publications, 102 Woodglen Court, Flat Rock, NC 28731. E-mail: faithwalk@brinet.com.

5. Peck, *The Road Less Traveled,* 15. These three words constitute the entire opening paragraph of Peck's book.

## POEMS

1. May Sarton, "The Autumn Sonnets," in *Selected Poems of May Sarton,* ed. Serena Sue Hilsinger and Lois Brynes. This poignant but instructive poem by May Sarton is one of many splendid poems and writings also included in the anthology edited by Marilyn Sewell, *Cries of the Spirit* (Boston: Beacon Press, 1991).

2. Henry Van Dyke, "God of the Open Air," in *Arbor Day,* ed. Robert Haven Schauffler (New York: Moffat, Yard & Co., 1909), 90–91.

# HELPFUL RESOURCES

## PROGRAMS

Alzheimer's Association (formerly ADRDA): The only national voluntary organization founded to conquer AD through research and to provide education and support for persons who must live with this disease, their families, and caregivers. They offer aid in finding professional and community services, legal and financial help, and assistance in meeting lifestyle needs, as well as opening avenues for clinical drug trials. More than two hundred chapters exist throughout the country to help the nineteen million adults caring for loved ones with AD. For information on the chapter nearest you, phone 800-272-3900. The national office is located at 919 N. Michigan Ave., Suite 1000, Dept. H, Chicago, IL 60611-1672. Fax: 312-335-1110. Donations are appreciated to help support their work.

Alzheimer's Support Groups: Though a network of Alzheimer's Association support groups exists throughout the country (see above), other groups are not directly related to them financially. These groups are sponsored by various organizations (often churches or social service agencies) or persons, or they are organized by volunteer leadership. Such groups have sprung up in every state to help people learn to cope with day-to-day problems and to share fellowship with others.

Disability Insurance: Provided by Social Security for workers who become unable to perform substantial work because of a physical or mental disability prior to age sixty-five.

Exchange Support: Similar to baby-sitting co-ops, this arrangement involves taking turns keeping two impaired persons for a day, freeing the other caregiver. You might offer a college student a free room in your home in exchange for a specified number of hours of help with the afflicted person. Be creative. It requires explicit and open communication between bargaining participants.

Home Health Agencies: Private, nonprofit, and state-supported agencies that provide in-home health care services. Check the Yellow Pages under Home Health Services.

Independent Companions: Secured by advertising in local papers or by contacting churches or social services departments. Ask for references. Clear, straightforward, and open communications with such helpers are crucial to the success of this arrangement.

Info-Line: Most areas have such a source of information and referral. Call information for the number in your area.

Internal Revenue Service: 800-829-1040.

Medicaid: Known as Title 19, a federally subsidized, state-administered assistance program designed for the very poor. Eligibility is based on income and assets. Ask about Title 20 services, a special Medicaid waiver, which in some states provides help with cost of in-home custodial care.

Medicare: Known as Title 18, a federal insurance program for people over sixty-five that is geared to specialized treatment of short-term, acute conditions. At this writing, it does not provide help with cost of long-term custodial care.

Senior Centers: If your town has a senior center, go introduce yourself and explain your situation. See what services they might offer—hot lunch programs, day care, transportation, medical, dental and foot care, tax assistance. Friendly people staff these places and are there to help you.

State and Local Departments of Aging: Excellent sources for information about problems concerning older adults. Often listed in the colored pages of the phone book along with other government agencies. Ask for information with names and numbers of agencies and support services. Inquire about a state coordinating agency (usually connected to the State Department of Health Services). One could ask about availability of free or modest-cost legal assistance and counseling.

State Department of Health and Human Resources: Administers social service programs through local offices.

State Department of Income Maintenance: Administers Medicaid, supplemental income, food stamps.

Supplemental Security Income (SSI): A federal disability assistance program administered by the Social Security Administration. Provides monthly income to disabled or persons over sixty-five who need financial assistance. Eligibility based on income and assets.

## PRINTED AND VISUAL MATERIALS

*Books*

Alzheimer's Association. *Male Caregiver's Guide.* Order by writing to the Des Moines chapter, 1200 Pleasant Street, Des Moines, IA 50309, or call 800-738-8071. The guide is $15, includes shipping.

Ballard, E., and C. Poer. "Sexuality and the Alzheimer's Patient," 1993, Bryan ADRC, Box 3600, Duke Medical Center, Durham, NC 27710. In North Carolina only, call 800-672-4213. Addresses the sometimes troublesome problems or concerns about sexuality that caregivers must cope with, including the well-being of the afflicted one.

Bausell, R. Barker, and Michael A. Rooney. *Nursing Homes: How to Evaluate and Select a Nursing Home.* Emmaus, Pa.: People's Medical Society, 1983. This is one of the most complete and helpful aids to selecting a nursing home that I have found. The address of the People's Medical Society is 14 E. Minor Street, Emmaus, PA 18049.

Bell, V., and D. Troxel. *The Best Friends Approach to Alzheimer's Care.* Baltimore: Health Professions Press, 1997.

Burger, S. G., V. Fraser, S. Hunt, and B. Frank. *Nursing Homes: Getting Good Care There.* Washington, D.C.: National Citizens Coalition for Nursing Home Reform, 1996. The coalition's address is 1424 16th St., NW, #202, Washington, DC 20036-2211.

Cohen, Donna, and Carl Eisdorfer. *The Loss of Self: A Family Resource for the Care of Alzheimer's Disease and Related Disorders.* New York: W. W. Norton & Co, 1986. This outstanding reference for the Alzheimer's caregiver is complete in scope and written with sensitivity.

Coughlan, P. B. *Facing Alzheimer's: Family Caregivers Speak.* New York: Ballantine Books, 1993.

Dass, Ram, and Paul Gorman. *How Can I Help?* New York: Alfred A. Knopf, 1985. Refreshment and relief for any caregiver who is on the brink of burnout. Includes a nurturing and supportive collection of short stories by caregivers.

Davies, H., and M. Jensen. *Alzheimer's: The Answers You Need.* Published in 1998 by Elder Books, this book can be ordered by calling 800-909-COPE or 415-488-9002. E-mail: elder@nbn.com. $10.95. This book is written for the person who has AD.

Eddy, Robert Merrill, and Kathy Wonson. *Writing with Light: Meditations for Caregivers in Word and Image.* Cleveland: United Church Press, 1997. An oasis of powerful images and sensitive writing for those whose spirits need a boost. The book is organized in short and simple enough passages to be shared with the afflicted loved one, stimulating pleasant memories or conversations drawn from past experiences or helping unspoken grief to emerge. A splendid gift for a caregiver.

Friedman, Jo-Ann. *Home Health Care: A Complete Guide for Patients and Their Families.* New York: W. W. Norton & Co., 1986. This manual is useful to Alzheimer families in defining needs, teaching methods of caregiving and preventative health care, and finding appropriate help.

Gwyther, Lisa. *Care of Alzheimer Patients: A Manual for Nursing Home Staff.* Durham, N.C.: American Health Care Association and the Alzheimer's Association, 1985. See also, *You Are One of Us: Successful Clergy/Church Connections to Alzheimer's Families.* 1995. Available from Duke Family Support Program. Call ADEAR: 800-438-4380.

Horne, Jo. *Caregiving: Helping an Aging Loved One.* Long Beach, Calif.: American Association of Retired Persons, 1985. An empathetic guide to meeting the challenge of caring for older persons. A broader look at caregiving.

Kelly, William E. *Alzheimer's Disease and Related Disorders: Research and Management.* Springfield, Ill.: Charles C. Thomas, 1984.

Mace, Nancy L., and Peter V. Rabins, M.D. *The 36-Hour Day.* 2d ed. New York: Warner Books, 1991. This work continues to be a classic for caregiving families.

Manning, D. *When Love Gets Tough: The Nursing Home Decision.* Hereford, Tex.: Insight Books, 1988. These reflections from a minister about his decision to place his mother in a nursing home could be helpful to other clergy and families as well.

Powell, Lenore S., and Katie Courtice. *Alzheimer's: A Guide for Families.* Reading, Mass.: Addison-Wesley, 1983. This book is an especially helpful source for guidance in coping with the later stages of AD.

Sheridan, Carmel. *Failure Free Activities for the Alzheimer's Patient.* Oakland, Calif.: Cottage Books, 1987. The coordinator of dementia care in a large nursing home complex in Trumbull, Connecticut, finds this book her most frequently used printed resource.

Susik, D. H. *Hiring Home Caregivers.* San Luis Obispo, Calif.: Impact Publishers, 1995. Call 800-246-7228.

Wells, Ronald V. *Spiritual Disciplines for Everyday Living.* Bridgeport, Conn.: RDC Books, 1998. Write to 3030 Park Avenue, 9W9, Bridgeport, CT 06604.

### Periodicals

The materials that follow are available at most medical resource libraries.

*American Journal of Alzheimer's Care and Related Disorders.* This quarterly journal focuses entirely on the problems of AD. It is published by Prime National Publishing Corp., 470 Boston Post Road, Weston, CT 02193.

Davis, Ann, Marcella Nagelhout, Margaret Hoban, and Brenda Barnard. "Bowel Management: A Quality Assurance Approach to Upgrading Programs." *Journal of Gerontological Nursing* 12, no. 5 (May 1986): 13–16.

Gwyther, Lisa P., and Peter Rabins, M.D. "Practical Approaches for Treating Behavioral Symptoms of People with Mild to Moderate Alzheimer's Disease." *Primary Psychiatry* 3, no. 12 (December 1996). This excellent article is full of specific suggestions for particular behaviors that challenge the caregiver.

Isaacs, Bernard. "The Great Incontinence Roadshow." *Israel Journal of Medical Sciences* 21, no. 3 (March 1985): 288–91.

Jenkins, E. H. "Homemakers: The Core of Home Health Care." *Geriatric Nursing* 5, no. 1 (January–February 1984): 28–30.

McCormic, K. A., and K. L. Burgio. "Incontinence: An Update on Nursing Care Measures." *Journal of Gerontological Nursing* 10, no. 10 (October 1984): 16–23.

### Other Printed Materials

AARP. *Staying at Home: A Guide to Long-Term Care and Housing.* 1996. This is a rich resource for deciding when you need help and finding the help you need. It also lists other AARP resources for long-term planning and care. If you live far from your afflicted loved one, see also their *Miles Away and Still Caring: A Guide for Long-Distance Caregivers,* 1986.

ADEAR. *Alzheimer's Disease Genetics Fact Sheet* (Pub. No. Z129). Summarizes knowledge about the genetics of AD. Call 800-438-4380 for a free copy of this sheet or contact the ADEAR Center's website: http://www.alzheimers.org/adear.

Alzheimer's Association. *Public Catalog.* Call 800-272-3900 to request this catalog of resources, which includes a wide variety of Spanish language materials. Many are free, others are available at reasonable cost. Especially notable:

(1) The Action Series brochures on specific topics such as diagnosis, legal issues, ways to help an AD family, communication problems, care for advanced AD with its difficult behaviors, problems of wandering and safe return, helping teens cope, planning activities with the afflicted one. (2) *Family Guide for Alzheimer's Care in Residential Settings.* (3) *Private Long-Term Care Insurance: To Buy or Not to Buy?* (4) *Advances Newsletter.* (5) *Safe Return Registration.* (6) *Activity Programming for Persons with Dementia.* (7) *From Theory to Therapy: The Development of Drugs for Alzheimer's Disease,* updated regularly.

Alzheimer Canada. *Just for You: For People Diagnosed with Alzheimer's Disease.* Write to Alzheimer Canada, 1320 Younge St., Ste. 201, Toronto, Ontario M4T 1X2. $1.00.

*The Caregiver.* A newsletter published by the Duke Family Support Program, Box 3600, Duke Medical Center, Durham, NC 27710. $10/year; free to North Carolina residents. Call toll free in North Carolina, 800-672-4213, or 919-660-7510.

National Institute on Aging/National Institutes of Health. "Progress Report on Alzheimer's Disease." 1997. Of greatest interest in this report on advances in AD are the sections on diagnosis and treatment and latest theories of prevention. Available from the Alzheimer's Disease Education and Referral (ADEAR) Center, P.O. Box 8250, Silver Spring, MD 20907-8250, or call 800-438-4380. http://www.alzheimers.org/adear.

Robinson, Anne, Beth Spencer, and Laurie White. *Understanding Difficult Behaviors.* 1996. Eastern Michigan University Alzheimer's Education Program, P.O. Box 981337, Ypsilanti, MI 48198-1337. This excellent resource is problem specific—angry behavior, incontinence, bathing, dressing, wandering, repetitive actions, wanting to go home—with clearly spelled out possible causes and simple strategies for easing the problem.

Tully, M., and M. A. Blotzer. *Surviving Today and Revising Tomorrow: Caregiving Strategies for the Alzheimer's Spouse.* 1993. Alzheimer's Association of Greater Washington, 7910 Woodmont Ave., Ste. 1100, Bethesda, MD 20814.

*You Are One of Us: Successful Clergy/Church Connections to Alzheimer's Families.* Available from Duke Family Support Program. Call ADEAR: 800-438-4380. Suggestions for clergy and churches to help their members who suffer from Alzheimer's disease.

*Wiser Now.* Better Directions, P.O. Box 13005, LaJolla, CA 92093. A newsletter for AD caregivers. Twelve issues for $24.95. Call 800-999-0795. E-mail: AlzheimEd@aol.com.

*Videotapes*

*Caring About Howard.* Duke Educational Media Services at 919-684-3748. A wife determined to keep her husband at home as long as possible demonstrates how she took care of him using respite care, support groups, and a paid companion. A twenty-three-minute documentary. $25.00, includes shipping.

*Family Support Groups: Help for the Families of Alzheimer's Patients.* Members of a support group in Mt. Airy, North Carolina, working to help one another. Gives insight into the benefits of belonging to a support group. Available from the Duke Family Support Program, Center for the Study of Aging and Human Development, Box 3600, Duke University Medical Center, Durham, NC 27710. $25.00, includes shipping.

Gwyther, Lisa. *Home Is Where I Remember Things.* Duke Family Support Program (see above). Used for training home care, day care, or residential staff who work with people with AD, this video is also excellent for support group presentations. It portrays three families who struggle with the problems of AD. $30.00, includes shipping.

*Internet Addresses for Information*

info@alz.org

http://www.alz.orga

> Alzheimer's Association: Inquire about free copy of their public materials catalog. Ask about a support group nearest you

http://www.alzheimers.org/adear

> A service of the National Institute on Aging for information and referral, research and publications

www.aoa.dhhs.gov/aoa/

> Government agencies and resource centers

adear@alzheimers.org

> Answers your questions about AD

http://www.geocities.com/Athens/1330

> Caregivers Resource Homepage

www.caregiver.org

> Caregiver Alliance

www.hcfa.gov

> Health Care Financing Administration (Medicare and Medicaid)

www.irs.ustreas.gov.

> Internal Revenue Service

www.aoa.dhhs.gov

    U.S. Administration on Aging

www.nih.gov/nia

    National Institute on Aging

http:www.nafc.org

    National Association for Continence offers information on management, services, medication, exercise, and frequently asked questions

http://www/ahcpr.gov/guide

    Agency for Health Care Policy and Research: Click on "Clinical Practice Guidelines Online" for new information on treating chronic urinary incontinence at home

www.aarp.org

www.aarp.org/taxaide/home.htm

    American Association of Retired Persons

www.nscic.org

    National Senior Citizens Law Center

www.seniorlaw.com:80

    SeniorLaw Home Page: Current financial and health-related legal news

http:www.naela.org.

    National Academy of Elder Law Attorneys

info@naela.org.

    Latest information on legal matters

www.ssa.gov

    Social Security Administration

www.dol.gov/dol/pwba

    Pension and Welfare Benefits Administration

www.noah.cuny.edu/aging/aging.html

    Ask about aging and Alzheimer's disease

www.mindspring.com/~eldrcare/elderweb.htm

    ElderCare Navigator

www.edwardjones.com

    Elder care issues

www.aoa.dhhs.gov/aoa/pages/finplan.html

    Online resources for financial and retirement planning

http://www.biostat.wustl.edu/ALZHEIMER/

    Washington University AD Research Center

"*Alzheimer's Disease* is essential reading for families struggling to care for a loved one with this devastating illness. . . . In every instance, descriptive vignettes from her own experience are coupled with a range of strategies for coping which are practical without being overly simplistic."
—Dianne Davis, R.N., M.S.N., Geriatric Case Manager, Dorothy Adler Geriatric Assessment Center, Yale–New Haven Hospital

"Ms. Adams writes with loving compassion for the victims of Alzheimer's disease and for their devoted and selfless caregivers. Against the background story of her own mother's illness and her father's struggle, her book conveys the human tragedy of this devastating disease, while offering hope and her personal faith to the reader."
—Sarah Schade, Fletcher, North Carolina

"When one opens this book it is like finding a friend who has 'been there,' a spiritual director and a counselor who is there to help us grow through an experience which might otherwise destroy us. It is the first book anyone should read upon encountering Alzheimer's disease in oneself, a family member, a friend, a neighbor, or a colleague."
—Lillie Margaret Lazaruk, Fairfield, Connecticut

"Our millennial world is—literally, figuratively, progressively—organized by connection. Alzheimer's disease is an ironically modern disease... because it is all about losing connection. At the same time, the best way to cope with it is to keep on reconnecting. [This] excerpt...

illustrates this point and the unique spirit of Adams's book: 'Mother tried to express something without success. Shaking her head she said, "I... can't...connect anything." Dad reached out his hands and took both of hers. "There, now," he soothed. "We're connected." '"
—Barbara Currier Bell, Milford, Connecticut

"*Alzheimer's Disease: Courage for Those Who Care* belongs on the 'loan shelf' of every pastor and on the coffee table of every home in which families are struggling to come to terms with [Alzheimer's disease.]"
—Edward E. Thornton, Ph.D., Louisville, Kentucky

"Anyone who cares about a loved one with Alzheimer's or related dementia and their caregivers will appreciate Martha's story. Her story is our story. Knowing how she faced the hard issues gives us courage to care for our loved ones with love and compassion.... If nothing else, the book makes you feel like someone is walking with you on this difficult journey."
—Rev. Barbara E. Barlok, Director, Silver Service, Cheshire, Connecticut